Acknowledgements

To help the reader, this book supplies many practical examples of good writing, of bad writing, and of bad writing that I show how to improve. Some examples were plucked from my customary reading in the fields of technical and nontechnical literature. Others were passed on to me by volunteers, whom I thank. Most of them came from the raw or published material that has crossed my desk in recent years: manuscripts from other writers and editors; papers turned in by my students; and, of course, the outpouring of prose in the ever-busier world of science and technology. Sometimes, to sharpen the point I wished to make, I altered the example; sometimes, too, I created an entirely new one. Consequently, I have credited the source only when this seemed appropriate or necessary.

Elsewhere, when simply quoting the facts or views of another author, I have given suitable credit at that point in my text. I need add only that much of the material in Chapter 1 is drawn from an article of mine, "The Bad Language of Science," which appeared in the Autumn 1959 issue of *The South Atlantic Quarterly*.

My thanks to all who have read this book in its preliminary stages and helped, directly or indirectly, in the role of devil's advocate. And one last, specific acknowledgement: to my wife. As an editor herself, Eleanor brought to the manuscript a helpfully fresh pair of eyes.

W.G.

NEW YORK, NEW YORK
APRIL, 1961

Acknowledgements for British Edition

The changes in this British edition have been kept to a minimum. The majority are "Anglicising" alterations suggested by the editors of the English Universities Press, publishers of this edition, and for which I am most grateful. These alterations concern choice of spelling and of idiom, and were made in recognition of the fact that the new edition, unlike the first, is primarily for British rather than American readers. In spelling, for example, "labor" in the first edition has become "labour" in the second. However, quotations from American authors remain unaltered.

As a further service to my British readers, the publishers have supplied a bibliography of books likely to be of reference value.

W.G.

MIDDLETOWN SPRINGS, VERMONT
JULY, 1962

Contents

THE LANGUAGE OF SCIENCE

THE LANGUAGE OF SCIENCE

THE
LANGUAGE
OF
SCIENCE

A GUIDE TO
EFFECTIVE WRITING
BY WILLIAM GILMAN

THE ENGLISH UNIVERSITIES PRESS LTD
102 NEWGATE STREET · LONDON EC1

PRINTED IN THE UNITED KINGDOM BY
ELLIOTT BROTHERS AND YEOMAN LTD., LIVERPOOL
FOR THE ENGLISH UNIVERSITIES PRESS LTD., LONDON

1

THE LANGUAGE OF SCIENCE

LET us talk shop about the kind of writing that is more or less technical in content. And let us start off by establishing a rule. It is this: The rules of writing are not tyrannical; you may break them. This presupposes, of course, that you know what you are doing, that you are thinking clearly and using common sense, that you are not merely being illiterate. *[Self contradictory.]*

The rule I happen to be breaking now is one followed dutifully by too many who write in the increasingly important language of science. This rule is a nuisance to everybody who must read their writing. It declares that one should start off with a statement of the problem; and that, towards the end, one should provide something in the nature of "Conclusions," "Recommendations," "Summary" or "Findings."

Note that I have done the reverse. I did not begin by setting up the problem. The problem is _bad_ writing, and we can be sure that it is important enough—but it will be marching with us all through this book. And, after all, it is solutions we want. So, remembering my own days as a science student and then as a chemist, and drawing upon my experience as a writer and an editor, I started by offering the outline of a solution. In doing so, I was using what professionals call a "lead." That is, the first paragraph introduced *[WHAT IS BAD WRITING]*

3

the tone and content of the book. The lead could have been in the
form of a question, or an anecdote, or perhaps an apt quotation
from Bartlett. Here it was functional. It briefly described a course
of action and stated the requirements.

IT IS

DULL &
OBSCURE

No, this isn't failure to start with first things first. The problem
is already notorious. This problem—writing that is not only dull
but obscure—is being shouted at us from all sides, by deans of
engineering as loudly as by liberal-arts educators, by research
laboratories and by industry. The time has come to state the
problem in these terms: What can we do about it?

Suppose I followed scientific protocol and cagily, with the
cautious reservations and disclaimers that scientists themselves de-
ride, buried my opening statement at the end. It would be found
eventually—technical people have learned how to prowl through
a paper to determine whether it's worth reading. Very well then,
why not place it at the front in the first place, and gain the reader's
good will?

Is this, then, a rule? In most circumstances, yes. But again,
let us leave dogma for the dogmatists. Like other rules of effective
writing, this one isn't a rule because it is Holy Writ copied from a
stone tablet. Go on placing the main statement at the end of a
learned paper, if you insist, but be sure this isn't done mainly to
supply a cloak for either deliberate ambiguity or muddy meaning.
Though buried at the end, the statement should be so written that
it could stand boldly at the beginning.

The excuse for the
cover the main is
first things first.

But it is at least
that.

Failure is never
interesting.

Boldness, of course, is not <u>merely</u> another word for sensationalism. The statement can be just as important if it announces one
small step forward—<u>or even failure.</u> After all, not every report to
management or to a professional society proclaims a triumphant
breakthrough. A report can be completely significant, interesting—
and honest—if it starts: "After 10,000 man-hours of investigation,
we are still unable to state definitely that human beings or other
forms of animal life exist elsewhere in the universe."

The boldness of clarity, then, is our goal—clarity in sentence
and paragraph, clarity in organization of the whole. Clarity is
demanded of the person writing in the fields of science and technology. Clarity is also required from the many others who don't
work inside those fields but have to deal with them.

Clarity first. After that be a virtuoso if you like. Fancy flourishes are not forbidden. The only rigid ban is upon deliberate obfuscation or esoteric writing: James Joyce's *Finnegans Wake* cannot be your model. Urbanity, dramatics, whimsy, Samuel Johnsonian sentences, short explosive ones—these are matters of individual style, and there are some technical people who use such extras skilfully. But the crying need is for competent writing rather than for "lit'ry" literature.

Whether in press releases, magazine articles, professional-society papers, technical books, research proposals, or simply progress reports to management, the need is for clarity, clarity.

This need spans all walks of life. Our hopes, and our worries, too, feed from day to day upon what science and technology are ready to announce or propose next. Some of us are familiar enough with the language of science to take it raw and eventually get through it somehow. Many more of us must rely upon the inter-preters supplied by research groups and the communications industry.

In either case, science and technology cannot be allowed to stew in their own bad writing. Management has to know what its technical men are talking about. Wall Street has to gauge growth stocks based on boron fuels, semiconductors. Madison Avenue's copy writers have to sell titanium, polyplastics. Pennsylvania Avenue's policy makers in Washington have to plan for peace and war in terms of millcuries and Mach numbers. And the rest of the people have a pressing need to know.

So we do indeed have a problem. Basically, it lies on the door-step of the scientific and engineering people. For convenience, I lump these together as "technicians" (not an entirely satisfactory label, but the best available, as I will explain later) because "pure" science and "applied" engineering have become that distinctly twentieth-century phenomenon, the closely co-operating R & D (Research and Development) team.

Whether technicians write for other technicians or for non-technicians, the approach to understanding bumps into the same obstacle. The language here is basically a written language— it has to be. But where are the technicians who are competent to handle it? The experience of those of us who edit this writing shows too few able to get past muddy jargon and slide along on a stream of clear English. And the nontechnician who has to work with such material is not necessarily better than the technician, partly because of the condition in which the material reaches him, partly because of his own limitations. Obscure writing is not a monpoly of the technical people.

The writing in any political party's platform requires some degree of muddiness. It may not be clear from a modern sermon whether the preacher believes literally in hell-fire. Advertising writers deliberately court a *double entendre* in "the cigarette designed for men that women like." A prominent book reviewer starts his article with "Once upon a time when I was very young, I used to read books stretched out in a deck-chair. . . ."

But the accuracy required of the technician demands that he, not the books, be in the deck-chair. When he writes "There was a break in the pipe which caused the leak," the sentence is bad enough; had it been wrapped in typical jargon, it would have been quite hopeless—and typical.

This isn't quibbling by an imaginary Miss Thistlebottom, ruler of the rules of grammar, or a call upon science to scale the heights of gifted prose. Involved here is the communication of vital information. The bad language of science—its bewildering syntax and other faults of grammar, its less-than-forthright exposition, its substitution of cant for vocabulary—is paralysing that communication.

The problem leads not only to technological devices that won't work, but to an inability to discuss intelligently such political and social questions as the danger from radiation poisoning. The problem has become bolder in outline, and the communications industry has joined educators in sounding alarms, but it has not risen as suddenly as some of the calls to arms would indicate.

When the novelist James T. Farrell says, "Good, clear technical writing is essential now for society," he is echoing the warning by Sir James Barrie, "The man of science appears to be the only person who has something to say just now, and the only man who does not know how to say it," and by H. G. Wells, "Human history becomes more and more a race between education and catastrophe."

Communication requires, of course, adequacy in both transmitter and receiver. When a Purdue University poll reports that 40 per cent of American high school students think that the earth is the centre of the universe, it is tempting to blame the nontechnician and the educational system that doesn't require them to take enough science and mathematics in high school and college. When the Department of Defence announces a programme to send living creatures orbiting in a satellite, it says these space travellers will be "mice and primates." Why "primates" and not "monkeys"? Because some tender hearts get as emotional about monkeys as they do about dogs and cats. Therefore, call them "primates"—and the science-ignorant public will not be weeping over the fate of monkeys. AND MEN, OH IDIOT!

But the technician's problem is not merely one of civic responsibility—of keeping the government and the public informed. Let us not forget that the technical world, too, within its own borders, is crying for escape from what Dean John Dunning of Columbia University's School of Engineering calls the "Technological Tower of Babel."

So we face the following situation: As a workman, the technician needs his typewriter or a secretary even more regularly than he needs test tube or oscilloscope. He must write proposals, progress reports, findings for management. And for the advancement of his art, and the recognition that gives him personal advancement, he must publish papers addressed to his own kind. But of how much use is this writing if it does not really "reach" the readers, if it is merely scanned and then crammed away into the already overflowing files?

We can be cynical about the situation, can echo Dr. Harold Urey's suggestion that, because so much of the literary output by scientists is useless verbiage, it should be handled by a conveyor apparatus that will take it to an incinerator. But this would destroy good kernels of wheat along with the chaff.

The bad language of science is responsible for an intolerable amount of time lost with needless riddles, and it paraylses the flow of information. For instance, the efficiency of research done for the Department of Defence has been put as low as 15 per cent; with the rest blamed on poor communication, misunderstanding of objectives, difficulty in getting help from the existing information, much duplication of work already done. And a government administrator has reported that, for a research problem in the

$100,000 bracket, it is cheaper to make a fresh start in the laboratory than to begin by researching the literature.

The situation can be stated simply enough. Writing is communication; communication demands clarity. But the intercom network of the technical world is crippled by illiteracy or just careless handling of the language. When these are superimposed upon slipshod science and engineering—the "hurry-up-and-fix-it" methods of sloppy craftsmanship—it becomes understandable why we have assembled satellite rockets that exploded at the launching pad, bridges that collapsed, fleets of bombers that turned out to be structurally wrong.

We are entering an age in which we will indeed play music of the spheres. But it cannot be done without writing that gives the right size of the nuts and bolts for spaceships, and tells exactly how much heat and corrosion they can endure.

Now it may seem odd that grammar and semantics should bewilder minds that have supposedly been subjected to rigorous disciplines and dedicated to objective, clear thinking. Why do the orderly processes by which the technician works out an equation in thermodynamics apparently fail him when the challenge is merely that of parsing a sentence?

And why does he usually succumb to the timid and usually erroneous *may* when he really means "This rocket *can* be shot to the moon"?

Is producing a correct antecedent for *it* beyond the capabilities of the person who has learned that $(mc)^2$ would give an entirely different value from mc^2 in Einstein's famed formula for the equivalence of mass and energy?

Admitted that many words are becoming debased, blurred. It seems hopeless to insist on a distinction between *shall* and *will, that* and *which*. Our bad ears now match our bad tongues, and we tolerate an identity of meaning among *assure, ensure* and *insure*.

But isn't it a bit astonishing that technical people, working so much with forces, are so blithely indifferent to the simple, yet important, difference between *affect* and *effect*?

True, the concept of antimatter now adds an Alice in Wonderland, mirror-image dualism that hardly simplifies Einstein's universe. Universes that annihilate each other, nuclear particles that do not obey long-sacred laws—such is the stuff that antimatter dreams are made of. But it is not only astrophysical philosophy that can tie the poor brain in knots.

Neutrons have become workaday particles. Satellites are assemblies of apparatus. Yet even when the average technician uses words and word components that are understandable in themselves, the composite becomes a typically unpunctuated, cryptic:

> All single furnace integral superheat boilers contain submerged type desuperheaters in the steam drum of naval boilers. Their purpose is to desuperheat superheated steam for auxiliary purposes which . . .

And that is a relatively simple passage. It is free of evasive tactics—the intentional ambiguity and jargon that betray the hedging too common in technical language. Its fault is of another kind. We do well to condemn governmental secrecy and other deliberately drawn curtains, but there is also secrecy whose veil is simply bad writing. Prose that can be quickly understood is a necessity for technicians confronted by not only the outpour of technical books, but by multitudinous technical journals transmitting an estimated 3,000,000 scientific and technological articles written annually throughout the world.

There is even a hint of evidence that constant exposure to the ordeal of desuperheat jargon causes lasting injury. The technician loses what reading proficiency he might have had. It has been found that the average engineer reads with comprehension at a speed of 200 to 300 words per minute—no better than does the average American male with less education. Even more surprising, in tests given to members of the American Institute of Electrical Engineering, the technical men averaged 200 while their wives and other family members were averaging 418. The tests were in two sharply different categories, geology and oriental art. Let us scorn art if we wish, but the engineers were 70 words slower in geology.

Reading as slowly as he does, even in his own field, the technician can hardly make a dent on his "required reading." So he looks forward to mechanized help, from abstracting machines, translating machines and the like. It is certainly within probability

ILLOGICAL

that machines will be able to translate correctly, word for word; will correctly spell *neuron* and *neutron*; will find a way to associate substantives, working through a logical progression—*proton, neutron, neutrino, antineutrino*. Certainly they will meet a crying need if they both translate and abstract, thereby delivering concisely bundled facts from foreign languages.

But such machines can be only electronically rapid idiots without a trace of initiative. Their fidelity will force them to repeat pompous pedantry. They will dutifully repeat the dignified vagueness of *may* when the word should be *can*. And, just as a computer will compound errors, or may blink lights of frustration when the technician tries to divide infinity by zero, the machines will be only dumbfounded when confronted with this appraisal of a new aeroplane:

> Having considerable fuselage ahead of the wing, C-133 exhibits when a sharp roll is induced to one side, then the other a lateral shaking which is definite enough to warrant either a firm stance against it or being buckled into a seat.

Nor could such machines, as a human might, catch and correct this invitation to disaster:

> The method of gaining access to any enclosure is to first open the master door that has power disconnecting device. After power is off, master door, then the others, can be opened.

We could go on and on this way, scourging the problem. To solve it, paying lip service to clarity is not enough. Superficially simple rules, such as always using short words, are not enough either—science often cannot help using long ones.

Yet clarity is entirely possible, and sometimes is found where least expected. Gobbledygook, for instance, need not always characterize the language of government, even when the subject is science. When Washington described the progress of its research in nuclear fusion, the "bureaucratic" statement was far more readable than the rewritten version published by the New York *Times* the next day. The original clearly demonstrated, whether or not you had ever seen a deuteron, that good science and good writing are not implacable foes:

. . . For the past quarter century, people have been causing deuterons to fuse. This is done with a suitable accelerator. A stream of deuterons is fired at a target which contains deuterium. Each bombarding deuteron encounters a number of other deuterons before it comes to rest in the target, but only a small number of the collisions are effective. Most of the bombarding deuterons are simply wasted without being transmuted. . . .

Such writing gives hope that it is not impossible for technicians to write their way out of pits as bad as Communist Party jargon at its dialectical worst, such as the press release that begins:

> The electrolyte is a solid ionic crystalline lattice where the cationic conductivity is enhanced by incorporation of a polyvalent metalloid. ‖

It also gives hope that the technician will find courage to transform "ratio of load to deflection" into "stiffness" and "causes loss of stability in directions transverse to the load" into "causes buckling."

If we agree that clarity is possible, then how can it be taught, and by whom? It is significant that the Society of Technical Writers and Publishers has two disputing groups—those who were originally writers and those who were originally technicians. The many new courses in science writing focus attention on the need for successful teachers. A technician can teach the lingo of his own speciality better than he can teach how to write. On the other hand, the purely literary instructor cannot talk shop with medical students, or decode the garble of the metallurgist and show where to plant hyphens and commas in "precipitation hardened titanium alloys, vacuum refined and degassed refractory metals and cold rolled stainless steel ingots, high tensile."

The same problem is found in the outpouring of books on the science speciality called technical writing: authorship by writing instructors who are insufficiently familiar with technical talk, or by technicians who lack the editorial-office approach to the writer-reader relationship. Memoirs by really professional writers are common enough, but an instructional book by one of them is a rarity. They are too busy at their own writing.

The result, too often, is a growing row of self-improvement books on the technical reader's shelf—and disillusionment. Such a reader probably does not know Molière's satire on syntax, but mathematics tells him there are 120 ways to arrange the same five words. And when English does not prescribe the one best way, he feels betrayed. This is the stage at which his disappointment may grow into contempt for writing, because its rules are not pat enough.

Here he forgets or has not known that modern science, too, has had to compromise with rigidity. For example, the dictum on conservation of matter is now quaintly ridiculous. And it was only recently that scientists agreed that the zebra is a light-coloured animal with dark stripes, not a dark-coloured animal with light stripes.

Therefore we might be more tolerant towards the anarchy in the field of commas, or in the world of hyphens—which has become even worse than it was when H. W. Fowler described it in his definitive *A Dictionary of Modern English Usage*.

To begin with, let us realize these are problems that no slide rule can solve. But there is always common sense, which tells us that "solid fuel system" is ridiculous and "solid bearing fluid" even more so. Neither the system nor the fluid is solid, so we need hyphens: *solid-fuel*, *solid-bearing*. Even the theatre marquees of New York's Times Square know better. They dispense with the hyphen because everybody will understand "Shock by Shock Confessions of a Sorority Girl"; but when titillation would otherwise be lost, they provide the hyphen: "A Swedish Bed-Bouncing Film."

Our approach, therefore, should be a practical one. "High-style" writing is not needed here, but clear writing is. Or, to sound scientific about it, we can formulate a reliable equation: Brain action, when based on a clear grasp of facts, becomes clear thinking; and clear thinking feeds clear writing.

It is the "when . . ." proviso that dominates the equation. Journalists as a rule are not gifted writers. They are content to be adequate in finding the facts and setting them down. And when the technician really knows his facts, has thought them through, then he needs only ordinary honesty and a fair amount of brightness. He can learn how to communicate, as professional writers do, by doing. That means willingness to make a second try. It is presumptuous to think that clarity comes in a first draft.

The technician's profession gives him an advantage. He is supposed to be careful, logical. Then let him be so in his writing. Each word, like the mathematical constant K, should have precise meaning. If it does not, then he does not yet know what he means. If it does, "part production" becomes "production of parts" and comma troubles no longer lead to the weird "Dr. Woodward . . . is Morris Loeb, Professor of Chemistry at Harvard," which tries to make us believe that Woodward is Loeb.

The technician's background allows him to compare good syntax with a valid equation. If the sentence balances, ambiguity has vanished: *it* refers to what it should, and the dangling modifiers are gone; the sentence is lean and direct, with its verb doing the right thing even if subject and object aren't clearly labelled; transitions are clean, sentence to sentence, paragraph to paragraph. Common-sense logic has organized a mass of words; the writer is learning to treat language with the respect he shows science.

He can become clear, which is sufficient. If talented in that direction, he can even become eloquent (like Willy Ley and Wernher von Braun clearing up complexities of the Space Age, and doing it in the English language, which is not their native tongue). Thus, a reader writes with verve to the editor of his engineering journal:

> We are inundating ourselves with junk. Science devises junk; industry mass-produces it; business peddles it; advertising conditions our reflexes to reach for the big, red box of it. To be sure, we are skilled junkmen. Our technological advance is swift and brilliant as a comet. . . .

Michael Faraday lived in an era when "style" was different. He had not heard of brisk sentences. But he, too, could write lucidly—and with classic gracefulness:

> It is the great beauty of our science that advancement in it, whether in a degree great or small, instead of exhausting the subject of research, opens the doors to further and more abundant knowledge, overflowing with beauty and utility.

We now begin to see that, to be accurate, one need not be boring; to be interesting, one need not compromise with accuracy; and that, with so much written matter clamouring for the attention of readers, it is physically impossible for them to be patient any longer with murderous prose.

The other thing to remember is that the bases of effective prose are the same whether you are writing a manual on how to instal a vacuum furnace, or promoting a new porcelain, or doing an article about cantilever stresses for a technical magazine, or reporting to management that you need more research money for a new type of electric computer, or writing the research paper I noticed recently on "Rectal Temperatures of the Bumblebee."

This chapter has given a picture of the problem in its various aspects, and has illustrated some of the ways it is being attacked successfully. Furthermore, note that as far back as the first page I began indicating how to concentrate on the job at hand, rather than be a worried slave of this or that set of rules. I wasted no time with preliminaries but immediately told what this book is about. And I have started many a sentence, when it suited me, with an *And* or a *But*. I remember my astonishment when a young editor said he was shocked to see that I had violated a rule he had been taught: I had started a sentence with *And*. I was myself shocked— to see the strait jacket he was wearing.

Are the rules, then, so bad? Not at all. If the expert seldom worries about them, it is because he can write "by ear." This is possible because the principles of good usage have soaked deeply into him. Good usage, in turn, is simply an assortment of practical tools for handling workaday problems. The rules are reasonably flexible servants. It is not their fault if they cease being the servant and become the master. Furthermore, the trouble is often with the amateurs who misquote the rules, rather than with the rules themselves.

All this concerns techniques of the trade, and I will talk about them in following chapters. But even gimmicks are most effective when used within the framework of guiding principles:

▶ Save time by spending a little more time reading well-written prose—its intrinsic lessons will soak in and become part of your own writing stream.

▶ When writing, take time to rewrite, because it is actually a wonderful timesaver—it straightens your thinking.

▶ Bend rigid rules to fit your own purpose—but in a way that shows you know what you are doing.

▶ Never forget the reader—in fact, before you set down a single word, be sure you have decided how much he knows, what interests him and, most important, how much clarification he will need.

▶ And when in doubt, it's common sense to use common sense. That is what it's for.

2

HYPHEN HORRORS

NOWHERE in punctuation is there a worse troublemaker than the hyphen. It seems such a little thing, yet the importance of this one short stroke cannot be exaggerated. When it compounds two words, it can change the meaning completely. But that is not all. Nowhere in writing are the rules more elastic.

This punctuation mark, then, becomes a challenge worth a chapter of its own. If the hyphen can be tamed by common sense, without our getting lost in labyrinths of grammar, so can other troubles with writing.

Forget for the moment that your main interest is in technology, and consider yourself "the average person." Sitting down to write a letter, you begin, "Great news! My vacation is coming and I can take the long planned trip to . . ."

Here your reader will stop—to question. Is it a *long trip* you are taking? Or have you been planning it a *long time*? Likely enough you meant the latter and should have supplied a hyphen: *long-planned trip*.

Or suppose that you are very avant-garde. Now you are linking words, but again shunning hyphens. So, when you go to the corner drugstore, it's the *cornerdrugstore*. There you *sitdown* on a *revolvingstool* and study the *menudisplay*. No semantical harm done. The reader can struggle through to the meaning whether such combinations are valid or not.

But the menu is not modern, nor is it old-fashioned. It just cannot make up its mind. You feel sure it doesn't really mean "Three Decker Sandwiches" for 75 cents because obviously it's selling a single sandwich that has three decks. Then why not say "Three-decker Sandwiches"? It goes on with "Homemade Ice Cream." But why not "Home Made Ice Cream" and be consistent? Or "Homemade Icecream"? And why "To-day—Virginia Ham" when most of us now write the word "*today*" and, rain or shine, it usually becomes *tomorrow*? Still, there is no harm done, except that we marvel at such inconsistency and write off the menu's writer as illiterate or very sloppy.

Now suppose that you read three announcements about the same new product. One is offering "a light-transparent layer of ceramic"; the second, "a light, transparent layer of ceramic"; the third (scorning any punctuation), "a light transparent ceramic layer."

In that simple example you do indeed run into trouble. Only the first two versions are as exact as technical language should be. But they say different things. No. 1, though wastefully tautological, is clearly offering a layer that transmits rays of light. No. 2 offers a layer too, but this layer, besides being transparent, doesn't weigh much.

Such hyphen troubles constantly plague both writer and reader in all fields of science and technology. Instead of clarity they give us word games—ambiguities that ruin the close tolerances of mechanics and the precise results of research. The confusion slows down reading, bogs down meaning, drives perfectionists to the ulcer specialists. The technical reader wastes valuable time crawling over such obstacles; the layman simply stops in despair.

Let us put the problem in proper perspective. True, the hyphen is just a punctuation mark; also, habits in writing do change, both with ordinary usage and with the impact of new words from the laboratories and from the men scouting outer space. Often, the problem just drifts away. The *New-England* of Colonial days is equally understandable as the *New England* of today. We changed from *servo motor* to *servo-motor* and have simplified to *servomotor*. *Nose-cone* and *nose cone* end up as *nosecone*. The meaning remains the same and quite clear. And if the result of combining becomes too unwieldy we can readjust and strip *magnetohydrodynamics* down to *hydromagnetics*.

None of this is new. Even when Madison Avenue strains for an attention-getting collision word such as *oneofakind*, we merely see the growing pains of the language, which is a living, changing thing. The new word of today becomes tomorrow's cliché.

But when the growing pains cause sharp mental distress to the reader, that's something else.

THREE ROADS TO CONFUSION

The compounding of words can be handled three ways, and each is potential trouble.

1. *Omit a needed hyphen* and you get an ambiguous puzzler. One newspaper tells us about "a delegation of small business men" (but are they really small men?). Another writes about "a poor State executive" (is it he who is poor, or the State?). This is the same two-faced language that gives us *heavy duty saw* and *ideal gas law*. Most mechanically minded people can understand the true meaning of the first; but the second will easily deceive even the technician if he doesn't happen to know physical chemistry.

2. *Use too many hyphens,* and not only does the page turn discouragingly black with them, but your message becomes cryptic with jawbreakers like "Life-vest storage is provided by a bottom-attached pocket on one of the plastic cushion-suspension straps." And imagine how that would sound if delivered orally, at open meeting or over the radio. Even simpler combinations give trouble orally. For example, Columbia University announces its "Great Teacher Award." The newspaper reader must puzzle: a great award for teachers, or an award for great teachers? If the latter, it should read "Great-Teacher Award." But over the radio, the listener would not hear the hyphen; so the phrase should be recast, "Award for Great Teachers."

3. *Overdo the solid form,* as in *menudisplay*, and you have monstrosities pleasant to read only as parody. For example, the popular "Spaceman's Lexicon" which translates *warhead* into *das laudenboomer* and *nuclear warhead* into *das eargeschplitten laudenboomer*.

RULE-BREAKERS AND CONFUSION-MAKERS

But do not some rules of good hyphen conduct exist? Yes, they are found in various books about writing. The style manual prepared by the University of Chicago even devotes a dozen pages to hyphen rules. However, such guides have a common failing in that they do not focus on the important, growing needs of science. Moreover, even in their generalized form, they confess inadequacy. Thus, as good and concise a set as any is found under "Compounds and Hyphenation" at the back of *Webster's New Collegiate Dictionary*. But it begins discouragingly, "Though authorities differ widely . . ."

And earthy H. L. Mencken, who would have been the first to point out that a soldout house is not the same as a sold outhouse, nevertheless fills pages of his *The American Language* with inconsistencies: The same page that talks of "American milk-wagon drivers" goes on to speak, without hyphen, of "used car dealers and such idealists."

Let us try another approach, this time the duties of the hyphen. There are several that give no difficulty. For example, the hyphen indicates a break between syllables of a longish word that must be continued to the next line. The only tool needed here is a dictionary.

Of far more interest to writers is the hyphen's troublesome role as a separator in compounding. Here, the more practical questions boil down to these:

▶ What do you do when one element of the compound is a combining form? This need not be frightening. If the combining form is a specific, such as *gyro*, *ferro* or *bio*, it is easy to recognize and generally gives no trouble when "run in" to form a solid word without hyphen. For example: *gyrocompass*, *ferromagnetic*, *bioelectronics*.

The same is true of standard prefixes. We write *nonscientist* and *noncrystalline* with as much impunity as *nonskid* and *nonstop*. Even as conservative (and valuable) a style manual as that published by the United States Government Printing Office merely lists the obvious need for the hyphen in a word like *inter-American* (where the second element cannot lose its capital letter) and then states that no hyphen is needed for all other words preceded by the prefix *inter*.

And there is certainly little trouble, either, with suffixes: percent*age*, stain*less*, and the like.

True, we must remember that a *re-covered* umbrella is quite different from a *recovered* umbrella, and there are other relatively minor do's and don'ts. For example, the chemist cannot play loosely with a substance that must call itself exactly *1, 3, 7-octen-5-yne*.

▶ What do you do with the elements of a simply or frequently compounded noun? Here, too, the difficulties are not great because conventional usage is a sufficient guide. Both *volt* and *meter* are nouns. Combine them and they become *volt-meter*. After a while this evolves into *voltmeter*. Similarly with a familiar adjective appearing in simple combinations. *Black-bird* long ago became the solid form, *blackbird*. In all this there is no serious problem if we stick with conventional *bookworm* and leave *bookreviewer* to capable pioneers like John Dos Passos. And it is easy enough, when in doubt, to find the conventional in dictionaries, style manuals and books on writing.

▶ How do you handle elements of a compounded word when it includes verb forms, adverbs or troublesome adjectives? Here, where technical writing is most vulnerable, is where the language reels with confusion and we find freewheeling at its fastest r.p.m. Here is where the grammarian's concern with syntax, such as whether the word is being used attributively or predicatively, might be worth studying if only the rules didn't contain so many escape clauses. Here, then, you are put very much on your own. Is there no safety? There must be—or we wouldn't have so much capable writing.

Let us first realize that the twin problems, ambiguity and inconsistency, are not confined to only one side of the Atlantic, or to the age of nucleonics and man-made moons.

When Fowler assembled his *A Dictionary of Modern English Usage* (first published in 1926), he approached the problem half in anger, half in mourning: "The chaos prevailing among writers or printers or both regarding the use of hyphens is discreditable to English education."

He needn't have mourned. The chaos existed long before the twentieth century; probably it goes all the way back to the first grammarians and the first punctuation marks. And the mourning goes back too.

When Montaigne was writing, in the sixteenth century, he complained about the French language: "Who may hope that its present form shall be in use fifty years hence? It daily changes and slips our hands." And in Montaigne, as translated by his contemporary John Florio, what do we find? The Englishman dedicates his work to the "all-vertue-accomplished ladies," speaks of "a faire-gracious bodie," vows service for "many-many favours he had done me," describes "a kinde of bitter-sweet-prickling of malicious delight." Apparently his hyphens were well-beloved. But then, abruptly, we come on to "nature her selfe" and "sunne-set to sunne rising."

Nor had consistency become a jewel when a London newspaper in 1771 enumerated 78 ways "To Express the Condition of an Honest Fellow under the Effects of Good Fellowship." Therein we find the condition unhyphened in *top heavy*, *chuck full* and *half cocked*, but also described as *cup-stricken* and *pot-valiant*, and given the solid form in *castaway*.

And today, the same scholarly British journal that writes *steelmaking* also writes *to-morrow* and *a thirteen years old*. Such lapses are not first-degree offenses against consistency. We usually understand that *thirty one cent stamps* does not mean *31-cent stamps*. But the trouble becomes more serious when the journal wastes hyphens on words like *to-morrow* and *radio-activity* and then, apparently with none left, offers the thoroughly ambiguous "new type of cold cathode trigger tube" (cold tube? cold cathode?). Omitting the hyphen here has created needless chaos.

Sometimes jargon is excusable. For example, an American publication is stuck with the title *Journal of the Closed Impression Die Forging Industry*. And we certainly don't bother to hyphenate *natural history museum*, because we have all learned what it means. But *primitive art museum* confounds us. Is it a museum down in

Zululand or a museum that collects Zulu art? If the latter, it should be *primitive-art museum*. Or why not just *museum of primitive art*?

And if the problem is solved by transposing the words and inserting *of*, then why not more of the same? Why not go directly to the noun as a starting point, and then work back to the modifiers?

For instance, look again at *ideal gas law*. If it is two-faced and happens to be 100 per cent incorrect. *Law* is the noun, but the modifier is not *ideal* alone, nor *gas* alone. This is not an *ideal law* or even a *gas law*. The law covers only gases behaving as they would under ideal conditions. That is, *ideal-gas law*. The hyphen proves we know what we are talking about; it shows we are thinking in terms of *of* or *with*. If the writer was a bit timid about using hyphens, he could have been safe with *law of ideal gases* or *law dealing with ideal gases*.

There are other occasions when common sense shows how to avoid the hyphen. *Natural history museum* is one example. *Nuclear power station* is another. Strictly, it should be *nuclear-power station*. But omitting the hyphen creates no hardship. Even if our minds read those words in the sense of *nuclear power-station*, we end up with much the same concept: the fission of atoms provides the power from this station.

One of the best examples of how familiarity breeds justifiable contempt for the hyphen is the compound adjective *stainless steel*. Strictly, it should be *stainless-steel component* and *stainless-steel kitchen*. But we safely discard the hyphen because *stainless steel component* and *stainless steel kitchen* are as easily understood in their true sense as are *cut rate drugs* or *machine tool industry*. In fact, metallurgists often drop the word *steel* too; *stainless* is their shorthand for *stainless steel*.

Unfamiliarity, by contrast, breeds confusion. *Baby computer* needs no hyphen—in fact, must not have one unless you mean a *counter of babies*. But *high accuracy probe* needs the hyphen to erase any concept of altitude. And what of *heavy hydrogen reactor*? Laymen, and even technicians who are not in nucleonics, will think of heavy equipment. Only *heavy-hydrogen reactor* will correctly indicate a reactor that uses heavy hydrogen. Similarly, when *critical materials problem* means a critical problem, it should be written *critical materials-problem*, not *critical-materials problem*.

These are examples of that busy troublemaker, the compound adjective. The ambiguity could be fun: In the song "Purple People Eater," is he purple or does he eat purple people? But if you are a serious reader, and your field doesn't happen to be electrochemistry, try working out the United States Bureau of Standards' "free radicals symposium." Even the surmise that this isn't a conclave of subversives doesn't help much. Nor is cryptic condensation to be found only in three-word phrases. Try decoding "all welded aluminium offshore oil well drilling platform." It can be done—but it takes valuable time.

WRITING WITHOUT RIDDLES

Now let us see if hyphen problems need really be so serious. We have already noted that merely throwing in a hyphen is not the cure-all. The problems have to do not only with use or nonuse of the hyphen, but also with misuse and overuse. Would the answers lie in legislation? Perhaps, but not before we know whether we are sending our letters to *ex-Republican Congressman* Smith, who might do something for us, or to the lame duck, *Republican ex-Congressman* Smith.

And anyway, the need is not that desperate. Rules of good hyphen conduct are entirely possible. They have already been emerging, in shadowy shape, from the examples we have been discussing. Let us crystallize and assemble them.

Hyphens—Your Guide

1. The standard rules should be treated with respect—and caution. When they concern hyphens, they are artful dodgers. For example, a simple function of the hyphen is to prevent a confusing succession of letters. We are told to hyphenate a combination of words wherein the same letter occurs three times in a row (*bell-like* instead of *belllike*) or when the first element ends with, and the second begins with, the same vowel (*anti-isolationist*, not *antiisolationist*).

Yet nowadays we do use *cooperate*. Why? Because heavy usage has bred familiarity. By contrast, though the rules would allow *antiantithesis*, this compound is still too unfamiliar, too awkward, and it is safer conduct to be easy on the reader and write it *anti-antithesis*.

2. The test of familiarity is therefore one you should call upon constantly. We now dare to write *freelance*, *shorthand*, *setscrew*, without hyphens. And inasmuch as we write *clockwise*, why remain faithful to the dictionary that still prescribes a hyphen for the other direction? *Counterclockwise* will not baffle a reader; its elements are spotted easily.

Familiarity, yes. But who is the reader? Radioactive *fallout* is quickly recognized by any literate person. But where the mechanic can take *microinches* (or the abbreviation, *microin*) as easily as he does *homeowner*, the layman will be happier with two bites: *micro-inches*. Even the technical man, if his work doesn't concern *oxidation*, will be more comfortable with *non-oxidizing* than with *nonoxidizing*. The *no* twice in succession is awkward and the entire word at a fast glance has a feeling of *monoxide* about it.

Or take the sentence beginning "Bistable circuits use unijunction transistors . . ." The word *unijunction* is fair play, but *bistable* is more doubtful. It, too, uses a prefix. However, the impact of its prefix is not softened by a preceding word. A technician might have to halt at this word for a moment. A nontechnician might not identify it as meaning *bi-stable* until he had unsuccessfully rolled *bih'stubl* on his tongue.

So, think of the reader. Remember that standard rules may lead not merely to riddling but to utter ridiculousness. For example, you have the right to run in the prefix, but would you write *unionized* when you mean *un-ionized*? Others have done it.

3. The coinage of words requires special care because the criterion of familiarity frowns on overdoing the bizarre. For example, running words together is an art. Unless you are capable of experimenting with high-style writing, stay away from the James Joyce sort of thing. *Transistorize* is modern enough; *psychoceramics* (the study of crackpots) is amusing; *ideation* will only reveal your amateurism. Let others be first to try the combination *commonsense*, which I find in the same avant-garde piece that contains *povertystricken* and the perfectly legal but monstrous *pseudokingly* (clue: the base word here is *king*).

Regardless of whether you are running complete words

together in the solid form or adding a prefix or suffix to a word, be guided by common sense and don't shout with sensationalisms. The main rule is: Can the reader's eyes flit along the line without stopping and goggling? If so, the hyphen isn't needed. Similarly, when you do use hyphens, avoid the purely bizarre. In his *The Time Machine*, H. G. Wells used the noun *have-not* with clarity and literary skill. By contrast, a more recent writer's *the hit-aircraft* is illiterate.

4. The desire to save space is laudable but should not become writing that buries the reader in ambiguities and robs him of his time. The hyphen contributes heavily to such faults, but here the trouble is too many hyphens rather than too few. The overuse of hyphens may come from cryptic habits or from a conscious desire to cut down wordage. Such economy should be practiced with moderation.

I read the following, closely packed into sentences of the same complex paragraph: "thin-sheet-metal philosophy . . . closed torque-box structural members . . . under high-impact loads . . . vertical support-leg yields" and so on. Using too much of this is jawbreaking even when grammatically correct. Let in a little air. *Built-in straighteners* and *cam-operated clutches* are good any-where (as are *troughlike*, *headstock* and *sheetmetal*). But why "The lamp is flush-mounted on the wall" when "The lamp is mounted flush on the wall" says the same thing? It takes no more words, is clearer, and is active rather than weakly passive.

The hyphen can be a space-saver, yes. But at what cost in clarity? Remember that today's busy readers of expositional material are being preached at to read faster, even to learn how to skim. Remember, too, that the hyphen can often be supplanted advantageously by *of*, *with*, etc. For example, "rubber-impregnated nylon belt" is useful shorthand but many readers will slide more easily through the smoother "nylon belt impregnated with rubber."

Or take "the 6-foot-long-by-2-and-a-half-inch-diameter rocket." Why so much blackening with hyphens and so much suspense? Why not "the rocket 6 feet long and $2\frac{1}{2}$ inches in diameter"? Or take the suspensive hyphen itself. A sin constantly with us is the "corrosion, heat and cold-resistant material." To warn the reader that we are not speaking of *corrosion* and *heat* as such, that they

C

are not nouns but belong to compound adjectives, this is properly written with the suspensive hyphen: "corrosion-, heat- and cold-resistant material." But how much simpler to say "material resistant to corrosion, heat and cold"! This is the common-sense approach.

The standard rules, too, are helpful in holding down hyphens. For example, the *ly* rule works well with adverbs. Here is how. If we used the compound adjective, *fine precision parts* would bring up the old trouble, and we would need a hyphen to show it is the *precision*, not the *parts*, that is *fine*: *fine-precision parts*. But the phrase *finely precisioned parts*, using the adverbial version of *fine*, can have only the correct meaning, and needs no hyphen after the *ly* of *finely*.

Another handy rule, also concerning compound modifiers, discards the hyphen when the first of the modifiers is a comparative or superlative: *highest ranking primate, lighter coloured enamel*. Here, again, the rule has its roots in common sense.

Besides easing the reader's task there is a psychological reason for not overworking hyphens. Too many of them look frightening; they blacken the page with apparent obstacles. The more white space, the more inviting. A skilled writer, who uses many hyphens for effect, has a right to them, as in Wendell Willkie's "this now-you-see-it-now-you-don't impression." But when you read "competent, post-Fu Manchu-era Chinese performers," you end up as dazed as you do with this unhyphenated mess from the same newspaper, "Then he began an intensive door to door and free haircuts to bond buyers campaign."

5. The most common pitfall, however, is ambiguity that even slow reading cannot unriddle, that only the right hyphen in the right place can defeat. Here nothing can substitute for common sense.

We know that the hyphen is needed in *hold-down mechanism* and *fail-safe method*. But we also know that *bathing-suit* can now be written *bathing suit* because nobody worries any more lest we give an impression that the suit is going bathing, or that a dining room is a room that dines.

In advertising we can be even more emancipated. When we read "All Weather Drinks" on a sign our minds supply the missing hyphen because they have been conditioned to do so. When a department store advertised, "Introducing 21 jewel American made watches," that might have been troublesome. But it was not. To overcome ambiguity, and gain in display impact, the compound adjectives were identified in this fashion:

Introducing

21 JEWEL

AMERICAN MADE

WATCHES

And even when a publicist addresses his releases to "New Literature Editor," the same old editor goes on receiving them at the same old desk that handles new literature.

But in delivering the exact language required by science there is less room for play. Does *high strength steel filament* mean *filament* of *high-strength steel* or a *high-strength filament of steel?* Does *low pressure mist spray* mean that the *mist* or the *spray* is at low pressure?

The answers are no more complicated than deciding whether *criminal hunter* means what it says—a breaker of the game laws— or whether it means *criminal-hunter* (hunter of criminals). Similarly, the FBI had to direct its crusade in the 1930s against a breed of crooks it called *lawyer-criminals* (these lawyers had joined criminal gangs) because *criminal lawyers* already meant lawyers whose field was criminal law.

The confusion about adjectives is echoed in the confusion about verb forms. Take "Sharpening tools can be costly." Is it the cost of *sharpening* that is costly? Then say "the sharpening of tools" or "tool sharpening." Another way to indicate you are not talking about expensive *tools* is to switch from a vague verb form (*can be*) to an obviously singular one: "Sharpening tools *is* costly." But if you are dealing with an adjective form of the verb, then let it be "the sharpening tools."

Similarly with "tie rod linking A to B . . ." But we are not tying the rod. This must be a *tie-rod*, just as in *turning-rod* we have a rod for turning something and not a rod that is itself turning.

Again, our guidelines must be familiarity, consistency. For fellow professionals the bookkeeper can write "double entry account" and "job cost ledger" and "loose leaf book" with no danger (though why not simply *looseleaf?*). An architect can get away with a "2 story house." But the moment your writing is addressed to a somewhat wider audience, watch out. The financial report is hazy when it states, "Profit taking in the next two weeks . . ." Readers of articles on photography would have to be experts not to choke on "Once merely a photographic light measuring device and exposure calculator, the photoelectric cell . . ." Pity the poor reader!

6. Be consistent. At least, to your own self be true. Even the best writers are not always consistent. In general, however, there is a choice. Be conservative and punctuate tightly, or modernistic and punctuate more loosely. Wandering between the two camps raises doubts about your respect for accuracy. The same annual report by a large corporation speaks of "a $14 billion a year industry" and "the all-important final stage rocket"; in a single sentence we find "the full dimensional reproduction of high-fidelity music." And a technical magazine that has rediscovered the hyphen goes so far as to use it in the article heading, "Stainless-Steel Extrusions," but then lapses into old habits and polishes up the author into "stainless steel specialist."

Your road to consistency will be smoothed if you keep handy a list of frequently compounded words. Various style manuals contain such lists. Some are generalized; others are specialized to suit the needs of a particular technical field. Whichever one you select, it will be most effective if you consider it only as a framework. As the language changes, you will want to make changes in the list. Also, you may want to insert variations favoured in your specialized field. Such an emended list becomes your private consultant. It will save you from much pondering, and your readers will be grateful for the sameness of your compounding.

7. Above all, be clear. No stylisms, no rules, are as important as clarity. If the meaning is clear without a hyphen, omit it. Whenever lack of the hyphen would lead to confusion, awkwardness or a ridiculous interpretation, use it. If you aren't quite sure that the meaning is clear without a hyphen, that is a warning signal. So use the hyphen, and stay out of trouble.

3

THAT'S NOT WHAT YOU MEANT

LET us now dig out the causes of ambiguity and see what weapons we have against this treacherous enemy—an enemy because our kind of writing must be clear; treacherous enemy because it is so much with us, in so many forms.

Here is a simple example. What I want to say next is that I have already mentioned ambiguity.

I begin—easy words, easy sentence: "In Chapter I I mentioned ambiguity. . . ."

But, desiring both brevity and exactness, I have fallen into a trap. One of the *I*'s is a Roman numeral and the other is a first-person pronoun; it's all legal grammatically, yet it's ambiguous. The reader cannot help coming to an abrupt halt.

He has to puzzle whether I am referring to Chapter 1, or Chapter 11, or Chapter II—or perhaps have made an error in typing. Even a comma between the *I*'s might make the reader falter. So I discard them and write, "My first chapter has already mentioned ambiguity. . . ." NO IT DIDN'T.

Here, the only rule I followed was that of neatness—scrub out the muddiness because writing must make sense, and make sense easily.

Let's face it—we are all guilty of badly selected words and

In the first chapter, I have already mentioned ambiguity. ≈

29

badly turned phrases. The competent writer, however, does something about them. He hunts them down and replaces them with
something better. He is especially unfriendly to anything that
sneaks in to fog or even falsify his meaning. When weighing his
words, he remembers that communication must not make false
assumptions. It must not assume:

1. That every reader is smart. Some might not be. It is even
less likely that any reader is exactly your breed of specialist, taught
by the same professors, moulded by the same experiences. He may
not be a specialist at all. He may be the nontechnical boss trying
to read your report, the assembler trying to read your manual, the
layman trying to read your news story or magazine advertisement.

2. That the reader knows what you mean anyway. Science
is concerned with what's new. A small-town newspaper may dodge
scandal with the excuse that everybody knows about it already.
But how can the reader know about your new product or proposed
project until you tell him?

3. That the reader is patient. In technology, he cannot keep
up with the flood of reading that needs to be done, and hasn't time
to puzzle you out. It's much easier not to read your writing when
it gets obscure, just as it's easier to dodge the fine print of an
insurance policy. But you want him to read—directly or indirectly,
it is to your advantage that he read your writing.

Ambiguity is bad enough when it repels the reader. It's worse
when it brings ridicule, but can you blame readers when they
see: "The scientist presented an interesting paper on 'Idiots from
Birth.' There were about 200 present." Or: "Plastic makes a new
space saver for mothers who must travel with a small baby in the
form of an inflatable bathtub."

Still worse is the muddy meaning that invites tragedy. For
example, this description of a book on land mines:

I visualized myself trying to use this book out in the field, and I
had imaginings of blown-off feet, hands, and so forth, because of
the deficiencies of that publication. . . . The hardware suffered
for lack of good support information.

The comment was made by Henry E. Marschalk, publications
head of the Bureau of Ordnance, United States Navy. Speaking

at a better-writing institute held at Colorado State University, he went on to review the official report of an airliner crash. During a routine check, an elevator assembly had been removed from the plane. When it was reinstalled, both the reference manual and the catalogue of parts were consulted. But their message was ambiguous. It seemed to allow two ways of replacing a certain idler part. The wrong way was chosen. And after the plane took off, it promptly crashed, killing 16 persons.

Whether the result is comic or tragic, whether the cause is ordinary obscurity or an equivocal meaning, the successful preventive for ambiguity cannot be just an easy pill taken before writing. One such pill is the recommendation to avoid "big words." Let us, then, return to tiny, troublesome *I*.

Suppose I start a sentence "I is. . . ." Your mind immediately rebels; it starts shouting "I am. . . ." What I wanted to say, unhappily, is: "I is a personal pronoun." The cure is easy: "*I* is a personal pronoun." This shows I am talking, not about me, but about the word *I*. And throughout this book I follow the practice of italicizing a word when referring to it as an exhibit.

But what about all the other types of ambiguity? There can be only one over-all cure: a second look that will catch the obscurities in what you have written. And this requires a humble realization that nobody is immune. Ambiguity has been called the dishonour badge of the speciality known as technical writing, but science writing in general is hagridden by it. Some is just careless wording; some is the tactics of dodging; but it's all muddy.

Surely there was once a cave man who mistook a pitiful groan for a threatening grunt and finished off his colicky friend. Later, a Renaissance man, the great Francis Bacon, applied his analytical mind to this basic problem, which, of course, is lack of clarity:

> The human intellect makes its own difficulties, not using the true helps which are at man's disposal soberly and judiciously; whence follows manifold ignorance of things, and by reason of that ignorance mischiefs innumerable.

Today, writing is not only for the reader; much of it is for the listener as well. Hence the unique problems faced by the script-writer in radio and television. Elsewhere it may be optional whether or not writer or reader can pronounce the words correctly; over the air, mispronunciation can cause acute discomfort. Also, those who have written for radio learned long ago that sentences should be easier—the eye can reread, the ear cannot rehear.

Particularly devilish for radio and television are the built-in ambiguities. Writing's helpful hyphens and quotation marks seem to evaporate in the air. For example, "New York is served by a number of good-music stations" is baffling, even from the best announcer's lips. Does he mean good stations or good music? And "a light-chopping device" is not safe until changed to "device for chopping light."

True, television can not only inflect its voice but add gestures. Still, a gesture or even a sneer cannot substitute for quotation marks when you try to utter " 'secret' labels on the defence project." Nor can the announcer handle suspensive adjectives located too far from their nouns. "It destroyed the sugar-refinery and petroleum-well machinery" has to be recast into a form such as "It destroyed machinery at the sugar refinery and the petroleum well."

Beyond such special problems is the basic one that challenges all writers: lack of clarity. Basic, too, is the fact that when you know exactly what you want to say, precise words can be found and cast into precise sentences. Geology and chemistry, for instance, do quite well in disciplining their people to use correctly not only name-words but condition-words. A chemical coming out of solution is a *precipitate*. That is neither ambiguous nor jargon. Similarly with *flocculation* and *polymerization*. Each means its own kind of gathering together; neither is synonymous with the *coagulation* that turns milk or blood into thickened curd.

But physics and engineering have long had trouble with slangy words describing the damage that results when bad lubrication allows one metal to rub against another. Is it *galling* or *scoring* when scratches appear; is it *pick-up* or *seizing* when the friction creates so much heat that the two metals weld together? After editing several articles cluttered with these words, I felt that readers would welcome, as I would, relief from the ambiguity. The next such article carried an explanation, "This Is Galling," in which, at the cost of only 200 words, I allotted a precise meaning to each of the four words.

In short, our kind of writing must always be helpful; it has no room for Gertrude Stein's reluctance "to hold the reader's hat for him" and the antics of other cultists. Nor need we be ashamed of the company we keep. Even poetry—good poetry—has its disciplines. Robert Frost told a scientist one day, "Let's you and I compare science and poetry." The other said, "You mean the exactness of science and the inexactness of poetry?" Frost retorted, "If you mean poetry is inexact, I'm going home."

And in *The Elements of Style* we hear that master of non-technical prose, E. B. White, giving this advice:

> Be obscure clearly! Be wild of tongue in a way we can understand. Even to writers of market letters, telling us (but not telling us) which securities are promising, we can say, "Be cagey plainly! Be elliptical in a straightforward fashion."

Each to his own clarity. It's a toss-up whether crabwise crawling or cocksure nonsense is the more ridiculous. A few days after our bombing of Hiroshima, newspaper columnist Walter Winchell moved in on the hubbub with a "Things I Never Knew Till Now . . ."—this one about atoms. "Few motorists," Winchell lectured his readers, "realize that their cars are driven by atomic power. Gasoline is rich in hydrogen atoms. . . ."

And so is water. Are cows, then, driven by atomic power? Such circus-freak science did nothing to explain fission.

Fortunately, our government was this time alert to its responsibilities. Those of us who cared to know were soon racing through *Atomic Energy for Military Purposes*, the official and crystal-clear report by H. D. Smyth, of Princeton. For once, a remarkable development in history was being followed immediately by a capable book describing it.

But need there have been the Hiroshima holocaust? As remarkable as anything about the atomic bomb is the example of ambiguity described by W. G. Coughlin in *Harper's*. The United States had sent an ultimatum to Japan. When the reply came, it contained the key word *mokusatsu*. This could be translated two ways. Either the Japanese Cabinet was "refraining from comment"

—wanted more time to think it over—or the Cabinet was "ignoring" our ultimatum. Coughlin says we translated it the second way—and went ahead to drop the bomb.

The ambiguity in ordinary writing is usually not quite that world-shaking in its consequences. And neither is it the kind of misunderstanding limited to beginning or ending a war. It is easy to condemn the mechanic called in to repair your car or television set. His time-consuming blunders and guesswork are frustrating. But direct some of the blame at the instruction manuals and maintenance sheets that confuse him. He and his instructors are merely contributing to what technology has begun calling the high cost of goofing.

KNOW THE REAL ENEMY

Before you can weed out ambiguity from your writing, you must be able to recognize it, in all its guises. In this chapter, I have given some examples of ambiguity at work. Chapter 2 concentrated on the ambiguity problem with compounded words. (Also see Chapter 7, "Words That Say It Best," and the two glossaries of troublemakers in Chapter 10, pages 150-161.)

This much about ambiguity is clear. It is one of the faults easiest to cure—once you can spot it. To put this proviso another way: Nobody can hope to detect ambiguity until he has acquired the simple habit of giving a cold, hard stare at what he has just written. It is this "second look" that will spy something two-faced in:

Use this rifle once, and you will never use another.

The problem of securing wire is common to many industries. The wire should not be damaged by moving parts.

The first is ridiculous. Surely the writer wants to sell his rifle, not warn that it will blow up in your face. And the writer of the second surely is not lamenting the scarcity of wire. His next sentence shows that he should have substituted "clamping" or "fastening" for the ambiguous "securing."

But do not expect to conquer ambiguity until you realize that it is itself part of an over-all problem. If our goal is clarity, as it must be, then the problem can be called "unclarity" or obscurity.

Here we quickly face the question, "What is clarity?" This need not be as formidable as Pilate's "What is truth?" We can depend on examples of obscurity to enlighten us.

For instance, the word *ambiguity* itself is guilty of ambiguity. The dictionary defines it as an expression that can mean two or more different things; also as an expression that is indistinct, obscure. The first definition is clear enough. The second allows us to confuse ambiguity with such other sins as jargon, which smothers us with gibberish, and bad syntax, which hides the meaning under disorderly phrasing.

This is not the fault of the dictionary; it can only list the ways in which *ambiguity* is used. But this problem of definition need not bother us. It matters little where ordinary obscurity ends and two-faced ambiguity begins. The point is that until we can recognize obscurity, wherever and however this breakdown in communication occurs, we cannot devise tactics against it.

Look again at the Hiroshima example—certainly an indication of the perils lurking in translation. But there is this advantage with translations from a foreign tongue. By their very nature, they are more or less suspect; if we are wise, we know we are taking a calculated risk.

But what of trouble within our own language? Hasn't communication also broken down when ordinarily communicative and quite decent people cannot understand the same facts the same way? We find them ranging on opposite sides of the fence in controversies based on the findings of science; they argue passionately about organic gardening, radiation poisoning, cigarettes and cancer, fluoridation of water.

It may be true, as Beardsley Ruml said, that "Reasonable men always agree if they understand what they are talking about." The "if," unfortunately, cannot always be assumed. And in matters concerning science, faulty communication makes the "if" very iffy indeed.

Suppose you are a disappointed writer and want others to believe that you write only for yourself, that you don't care whether you have readers or not. That calls for looking at the problem in reverse. If you insist on repelling the reader, then choose obscurity.

For this, you can use ordinary ambiguity or other tools in the same kit.

One such tool is simple frustration. Here, the dictionary-maker is often guilty. We look up "cereal" and find it defined in terms of "grain." Then, turning hopefully to "grain," we find it defined in terms of "cereal."

That is a relatively minor nuisance. Obscurity can also be served in more memorable ways. I choose the following three examples because, in each, there were two losers—the writer and science.

A neglected miracle. Penicillin blazed the trail for the rest of the antibiotics. Alexander Fleming's report on the tantalizing behaviour of a blue-green mould was published in 1929. Not until 1941 and the needs of war was anything done about his discovery. This neglect has been called a disgrace of medical research. But can medicine be blamed? Fleming had not thrown away the nuisance mould, to be sure, but neither had he thought the implications through. And he had embalmed his findings in a typically dull report published in the journal of a typical learned society. A popularizing writer might have offended Fleming's dignity but would have given us penicillin much sooner.

"Case of the crazy Greek." When Nicholas Christofilos, who received his technical education in Athens, wrote in English, he was innocently demonstrating how bad "bad English" can be. Shortly after World War II, he sent a letter to nuclear scientists at the University of California, suggesting a new type of atomic accelerator. The letter was considered illiterate nonsense and ended in a waste-paper-basket. He continued his researches and hit on his plasma-pinching idea for producing controlled thermonuclear power. Another letter from "that crazy Greek" saw the waste-paper-basket again. Not until 1953, when Christofilos crossed the Atlantic and explained his dreams personally, was his pioneering recognized.

The ordeal of R. Buckminster Fuller. The mind of this creative thinker had ranged through many fields of science and engineering. In architecture, he scorned Man's plodding concept of post and beam. Noting that Nature is more sophisticated than that, he followed her lead and invented the geodesic dome. Here, as in the molecular latticework of a crystal or in the construction of a three-dimensional spider web, strength is increased enormously by a truss assembly using the guy-wire principle: tension opposes compression, and the wire pulls against itself. The resulting Fuller structures are at least as dramatic as anything Frank Lloyd Wright did with the cantilever principle. Yet Fuller remained relatively unknown for three decades. Though he wasn't at all hesitant about campaigning for his geodesic idea, the language he used was a strange one:

> Wave embodiments of cyclic experience appear everywhere in the accreted morphology of nature's omnidirectional, convergent-divergent, synchronous-dissynchronous, infinite plurality of pulsating controls of interactive events in principle.

Each of the above examples—bad presentation, bad English, heavy jargon—illustrates faulty communication. These trouble-makers will be discussed more fully in other chapters. I touch on them here only to show that they grow out of the same problem that gives us ambiguity—the problem of clarity versus opacity.

It is a problem that is receiving attention in every profession. Examining communication has itself become an important part of the communications industry. Its engineers once limited themselves to designing better microphones, electric relays, hearing aids; now they also delve in "information theory" and seek ways to stuff a computer's brain with as much memory as possible. The people in the fields of semantics and motivation research offer their own equations and jargon, and we even have charts on "How to Make Up Your Mind."

The problem boils down to fairly simple elements if we remember that communication is basically the interchange of messages. How well do you know what you're talking about? How well equipped mentally is the receiver—the other person—to understand you? And, of special interest to us, how well does your writing transmit the message?

An oratorio may not inspire you because you don't understand that kind of music, or because the chorus obviously doesn't understand it either. But the muddiness, the ambiguity, comes in transmission. If the singers are bad in enunciation, phrasing or tone, if the hall has bad acoustics, if the music coming over the radio must run a gantlet of fading or static, the best concert can be spoiled. Any of these contributes to what communications engineers call "noise." And when you transmit by writing, "noise" can wreck the message. The writer of "He brought in some pictures on a two-ton truck" really meant that the pictures showed a truck, not that the truck transported pictures.

This is the simplest, most treacherous type of ambiguity. It is like the faulty instructions that send a motorist down the wrong road. It is like a carpenter telling you to buy some one-inch boards. He is giving you instructions, but without explaining that such timber may be only $\frac{25}{32}$ of an inch thick after it's planed at the timber yard. Result: your do-it-yourself bookcase doesn't fit the space allotted to it.

The other type of standard ambiguity is less treacherous in that it does warn the reader. This, however, is not a virtue. Instead of receiving wrong instructions, the reader is suddenly confronted by a fork in the road. He has not been told which direction to turn and can only ask helplessly, "Just what does this mean?"

This type is often lumped with jargon and "big words." It fulfils the same function—it drives the reader from you—but it need not be jawbreaker words at all. It can be carelessness with easy words. Here are some standard ways to baffle the reader:

Failure to tell who does what

Wrong: Our department has contracted with XYZ Corporation to supply 7500 barrels of oil. (*Who is supplying, who is being supplied?*)

Right: Our department has given XYZ Corporation a contract to supply us with 7500 barrels of oil.

Right: Our department has contracted to supply XYZ Corporation with 7500 barrels of oil.

Mysterious antecedent

Wrong: This is a process to convert low-grade iron ore, which has been found expensive. (*The "which" portion was evi-*

dently tacked on as an afterthought, then a comma in-serted to cure the trouble, but the "which" still leaves us guessing. What's costly—the process or the ore?)

Right: This process to convert low-grade iron ore has been found expensive.

Right: This process converts low-grade iron ore, but has been found expensive.

Word with two meanings

Wrong: The process may be used in a production line. (*Here I have chosen one of the slyest offenders. Though it looks so innocent, two-faced* may *is forever trespassing on* can. *Possibly the writer really meant* may; *possibly he didn't know the difference. More likely, with a timidity found in much science writing, he was shying away from forth-rightly saying* can (*it's allowed, it's able to*) *and favouring* may (*it's possible, it might*); *or he was fudging—tricking the reader into taking his pick of meanings. The meaning of* may *has been so debauched in science writing that even if the above sentence is a true statement, it nevertheless needs clarification.*)

Right: The process can be used in a production line.

Right: The process will be used in a production line.

Right: It is possible that the process will be used in a production line.

Lazy wording

Wrong: It looks as though these ought to be checked against some-thing we already have; also I found it hard to tell who was asking who, what! Anyway it looks as though it needs co-ordination. (*The only right way here is to demand that the writer exercise some coordination on himself.*)

Each of the foregoing examples of faulty expression damages the writer's reputation in some way. In the eyes of his superiors, it seems that he is illiterate or careless, or has neglected to dig out the facts. If he is writing for people outside his own organization, he pays another penalty—loss of readership. His audience cannot be expected to do the listening, and the explaining too.

This damage is a pity because readers are driven by an ardent "need to know." For example, the record number of reprint requests received by an engineering magazine was for a series that had nothing whatever to do with engineering itself. The articles were called "Five Steps to Faster Reading."

The reader, therefore, starts off disposed in our favour. To hold his attention, then, how precise should we be—how clear can we be?

INSTRUMENTATION FOR CLARITY

Transmission cannot be perfect. The trouble starts with the human being and with H. G. Wells' warning that the mind crushes the truth a little. This happens in both writer and reader.

Moreover, it is human to be careless. The great Kepler, who gave us our concept of planets—and now artificial satellites—that move around the sun in elliptical orbits; this careful Kepler, who inflicted all 70 of his wrong hypotheses on his readers, to make sure they understood how much labour he had gone through; this fussy Kepler, who worked out his horoscope backward and found that his birth in 1751 occurred after a pregnancy lasting 224 days, 9 hours, 53 minutes—this same scientist, we are told, spelled his name five different ways: Johannes Kepler, Keppler, Khepler, Kheppler, Keplerus.

Machines are far from perfect too. How precise can we be when the things we describe deceive us? Two out of three car speedometers err—on the unsafe side. We only recently got equipment adequate to test some elements of Einstein's theory of relativity. The physicist has to admit that his best vacuum still contains millions of gas molecules per cubic inch. At Alamogordo, the critical test of the first atom bomb almost failed because two carefully machined parts didn't quite fit—warmth had expanded one more than the other.

On top of all this, we are reminded by Carl E. Lindstrom, a thoughtful newspaper editor:

> The writer is the creative manipulator of the most plastic, the most resistant, the most mercurial and yet the stickiest substance known to man—the written word.

Moreover, the writer, if he is a technician, must make himself clear to the point of specifying how wrong he might be—a problem that politicians and editorial writers do not face. He must state the tolerances—the amounts, in thousandths of an inch plus or minus, that each of two fitting parts can be in error—if the two parts are to work together properly.

But two parts comprise only a primitive assembly. A modern aircraft or missile system may include as many as a million individual components, obtained from over 500 different manufacturers. And error grows like an avalanche. If you have 100,000 parts in an assembly, and want it to be dependable two times out of three, then each part must be dependable 99,999 times out of 100,000.

A carpenter is usually satisfied if he is precise to within $\frac{1}{8}$ or $\frac{1}{16}$ of an inch. A butcher weighs to the nearest ounce. But a gyro wheel for space travel must be correctly in place to within millionths of an inch. The picture looks black indeed when we listen to Werner Heisenberg:

> The words *space*, *time*, *mass* are tainted with all the lack of precision to which we have to acquiesce in everyday life. . . . It seems that modern science should be preceded by a purification of language eliminating all ambiguous terms and concepts. But such a program could never be carried through.

Heisenberg is a noted theoretical physicist—expounder of the Principle of Uncertainty; winner of a Nobel Prize for his theory of quantum mechanics. He does not, however, live entirely in a dream world. His world allows for the pragmatism of make-do. Though their maps were wrong, pre-Columbus navigators did get about. Newton's laws are still legal if we don't travel too near the speed of light. Archimedes' laws of simple levers still form the theoretical basis of all load-raising machines and, says Heisenberg, "No doubt they will do so for all time."

Now we are back in the world of common sense. Uncertain instruments? sticky words? We do the best we can. There is no lion in the road; the road merely gets sticky at times. When it does, you warn the reader, so he won't get stuck. Where ambiguity would irritate him, a frank "I don't know" is sometimes refreshing

D

and often the most accurate analysis that can be made of a scientific situation. It also happens to be clear and honest.

Here's an example of warning the reader. The reader is yourself; I am reminding you of an explanation in the first chapter. There, citing the need for a label that would conveniently cover scientists and engineers alike, I apologetically chose "technicians."

You can now probably understand better why that is not an ideal label. However, coining such a word as "technists," "scieneers" or "scienticians" would merely add to the confusion, just as calling all these people "scientists" would further dilute an already diluted word. "Technicians"—and the posting of this warning sign—will have to do.

Somewhat similar is this problem: How shall I label readers of this book? Presumably you are in the professions or soon will be; and you want to communicate something of what's going on in science and technology. Such terms as "technical writer" exist but have become impossible—they would label all of you as writers of manuals and specification sheets. "Science writers" would be equally narrow.

Some day the suitable word may appear. Meanwhile, in this book, I handle the problem by avoiding it—and confiding in the reader. When referring to writing in general, I say so. When focusing on our kind of writing, I say "our" or "we." When necessary, I single out the technical writers, science writers, advertising writers, engineers and so on—even the report writer who has perhaps an audience of only one person, but an important one . . . his boss.

IT'S CALLED EMPATHY

Let's assume you have researched your subject sufficiently. Next, clarity requires that you know just what you want to say—the facts you want to give, the points you want to drive home. Let's assume you haven't been remiss here either. And yet your writing can be riddled through with ambiguity. Why?

Ambiguity comes from faults lurking in grammar and punctuation. It comes from straining for "style." It comes from vocabulary troubles: muddy words, clichés, "big words," jargon, bizarre words. The "noise" is much the same whether the troublemaker sneaked into the sentence or you dragged it in because it sounded learned or cute. Such are the visible causes of ambiguity.

Behind them stands an even worse villain. It might be called lack of empathy. It's the preoccupation with your own thoughts and words, the failure to be constantly putting yourself into the reader's shoes. You are commanded to Be Brave—write without equivocation; Be Simple—write without nutcracker words. More fundamental is: Be the Reader.

Does he know you mean "This adhesive is an answer" when you write "This adhesive is a solution"? Can he tell whether the experiment or the explosive is the antecedent for "it" in "The experiment gave a new explosive but it is safe"? Such ambiguity would confuse anybody, even your colleague. But remember that most readers are nameless and faceless. You must project yourself into their skins. The choice of audience ranges from laymen, who know less, to specialists, who know more, than you do. When you try to attract both types, then you are indeed in the empathy business.

Learning how to project yourself is neither hard nor easy. One simply does it—the way one practices being broadminded. Two guides are sufficient to prevent serious trouble.

1. Don't Overestimate the Reader. No sensible writer does. The reader may not be your kind of special-ologist, or he may be in a hurry. If both of you are laymen, you probably have different backgrounds. One survey finds Americans who think the earth stands still; another finds Americans who think cartoonist Al Capp is (1) a senator; (2) a Chicago gangster.

The reputable popularizer of science has to work much harder on his presentation than does the specialist, particularly that deluded specialist who thinks he has a captive audience. In his novel *Fire*, for instance, George R. Stewart describes the starting moment of a forest conflagration:

> Then suddenly, in a blue-white flash, for a period of some few millionths of a second, there poured through the tree between cloud and earth, a force equal to that of many powerhouses.

This is dramatic, and a fellow professional can also see the scientific accuracy with which the passage was moulded. But even

Stewart may have expected too much from readers of his best-seller.

He wrote his book more than two centuries after Benjamin Franklin's kite experiment showed what lightning is. Yet only a few years before *Fire* appeared, a man and his wife in America—both felled by a thunderbolt—were left on the ground to die. The onlookers were sympathetic enough. But they warned each other that helping the victims meant touching them, and touching them meant death. The onlookers knew so little about electricity that they were confusing a thunderbolt with a "live wire."

2. Don't Underestimate the Reader. This is at least as foolish as overestimating him and, of course, it may irritate him. Years ago, I made a trip through China's "Far West." I knew no Chinese words at the outset, and nobody in the smaller Szechwan villages understood English, even the pidgin variety. I would ask for a meal and place to sleep. The villagers would reply. Pure gibberish —they didn't understand me; I didn't understand them. Then, to make the situation sillier, they assumed that inasmuch as everybody must understand Szechwanese, I must be deaf. So they yelled at me, louder and louder. This didn't work either. Eventually, we had sense enough to settle on sign language. Cupping my hand under my head meant I needed sleep; motions of my thumb towards my mouth meant I was hungry—my hosts gleefully nodded, said *"che fan,"* and brought rice. Thus, talking with our hands, we settled on common words, and all went well.

The same condescension, with yelling at dolts and barbarians, is common enough in America, especially in some of its magazines. This accounts for much of the shrieking type and the noisy handling of colour that betrays boy editors at work. It accounts for some of the "simplification" that simultaneously irritates the brighter reader and throws the duller reader off the track. Thus, in a glowing promotion article in the New York *Times*, John Gunther began: "Before I visited Pfizer I did not know the difference between an antibiotic and a housefly. Pfizer, which rhymes with Kaiser . . ." and so on.

After you have correctly identified the reader, what you write has to stand on its own. Unless the reader is a close associate, you cannot see his puzzled look or hear his yells of pain; you cannot benefit from his challenging "What do you mean here?"

You have to be your own ambiguity-hunter. This is why I have given many examples of the fault. Sometimes you may find what seems to be a borderline case. That's enough—if it troubles you, it will most likely baffle the reader.

If it troubles you, that is enough. It's best not to waste time trying to find a specific name or spray for this particular bug. The cure is as informal as the diagnosis. If the word or sentence does not make sense, make it make sense—perhaps with a comma, or substituting another word, or dynamiting the sentence so you can build a clean, new one.

I shall later discuss such techniques in more detail. This chapter has been mostly concerned with learning how to recognize ambiguity and similar types of obscurity. In giving examples, however, I have also been indicating some over-all preventives and cures.

Less Ambiguity—Your Guide

Suppose you have just completed a first draft. Now look at it in the light of these defence measures.

1. Watch out for self-delusion. If you think that your writing is impeccably clear, then you still cannot recognize ambiguity. But possibly this is a blind spot that protects only your own writing. Turn your attention to newspapers and magazines. While reading them, use a pencil to mark each passage that makes you falter and ponder the true meaning. After a week or so, go back to your own writing. If it still sounds perfect, you are somebody quite special, but not necessarily a genius.

2. Picture your reader. You are writing, but for whom? The reader is tricky. He is a somewhat different personality when he picks up a research report than when he picks up *Reader's Digest*. And the pun *poisson* that might be slipped into an advertisement would be poison in a treatise on oceanography. Also think of the transmitter of your message. We've gone far past grunts and smoke signals; radio and television are examples of the many media of communication that introduce new ways to be obscure.

3. Strike out "important" words—every one that you put in

because it sounded impressive. This may sound like brutal surgery. It is. It is also the only way to overcome a habit that has made science so untranslatable and branded so many would-be writers as amateurs—or as fledglings trying to impress the boss. And if you yourself don't understand these "important" words, that's even worse.

4. Also watch the short words. True, they are generally easier for the reader—and for you too. *Polio* was a necessity—more specific than *infantile paralysis*, more easily understood and mouthed than *poliomyelitis*. But remember that short words, too, can reek with ambiguity. For example, in the space talk of the Space Age, *bird* now refers to missiles and earth satellites. But we also still have feathered fliers, from auks to zoo birds. To stress how ambiguous all this can be, suppose that the radar blips from a flock of genuine birds are reported as coming from a visitation of hostile missiles.

5. Popularization will help. You don't sound convincing when you toss your head and say it doesn't matter whether or not your writing is read. Remember that Shakespeare wrote for the people in the pit too. Furthermore, the stiffness of the formal scientific paper invites ambiguity. Darwin wrote that he was impressed "by the manner in which closely allied animals replace one another in proceeding southwards." He was being formally impersonal. But we don't know what he's talking about. He actually meant "as I proceeded southwards" and should have come right out and said so. There is nothing wrong with, nothing vulgar about words like *I* and *you*. And, unlike the Germans (with their differentiation between *Sie* and *du*) and others, we need not worry about distinctions between the formal and the familiar—we are all just plain *you*. Walt Whitman possibly overdid the you-and-I in his straining to clasp readers to his bosom, but this is only a matter of moderation.

6. But popularization needs brakes. Don't let it run away with you. The technician too often knows almost nothing about the craftsmanship in writing and therefore confuses popularization with "anything goes." This is a pathetic error. It often tempts him into decking himself out like a dancing girl in a mining town and offering to sell his virtue (highly inflated in value) to the first panting magazine that wants him. In popularization, all the rules of good taste, good grammar and clarity still hold. Take out the stiffness, yes, but beware of "just write it the way you talk." If we did, to paraphrase Shakespeare, how many of us would escape hanging? Leave rambling conversation and free association for William Saroyan and Tennessee Williams. Let them talk "off the top of my head"—it's not for us.

7. *Shun contrivances.* You're not writing for *Variety* or *The New Yorker*. To try makes you look a little sad, like the dancing elephant at the circus. Be fascinating if you can, but don't try to dazzle the reader with what the Elizabethans called conceits. Allusions can be intellectual fun but, unless you are a T. S. Eliot, play fair with the reader. If you want to hark back to the gears in "Modern Times" go on and identify it as a Charlie Chaplin picture of the 1930s—your readers may be of the next generation.

Avoid all puns like the plague, unless you're a superb punster and the pun clearly announces that's what it is. Puns are banned because their entire reason for existence is ambiguity. Furthermore, a clear "6 A.M." is shorter than "six in the yawning." Even clichés, supposedly dead and dull, aren't always guaranteed free of ambiguity. Combine two of them and you get Sam Goldwyn's "A verbal contract isn't worth the paper it's written on."

8. *Plug the holes.* It is the second look, or even reading the manuscript aloud, that is the lifesaver for most professional writers. This would most likely catch the unintentional pun that throws this electrical-power report into confusion. "Current needs are showing a perceptible rise." Another look would also have repaired the damage in a three-page announcement by the United States Public Health Service; it was full of talk about "impairments" without anywhere saying that they were physical impairments.

9. *Beware of favourites.* Get a divorce from words you may have grown too fond of. Engineers, for example, have a weakness for *flexible* because it covers so much. Too much. In "This gear tooth is less flexible than orthodox gear teeth and is difficult to make," the writer did not want to indicate it was less rubbery. Perish that thought! He merely wanted to say it was "less versatile."

10. *Sharpen, sharpen.* Precision is the most specific antidote for ambiguity. Precise words are found in dictionary and thesaurus—

that's what such books are for. And when composing a sentence, it's safest to keep closely related words near each other. That reduces the danger of trouble with antecedents.

If the sentence is hopelessly mired, don't try to barge your way out. Recast it instead of tacking on qualifiers. Even a relatively short sentence can quickly become hopeless. For example: "Jet aeroplanes are now a familiar sight to most people from the external point of view." The writer threw in the "from . . ." phrase as a qualifier. Instead of accuracy, he got ambiguity. Only recasting could save the sentence: "Most people are now familiar with the external appearance of jet aeroplanes."

11. But don't make it worse. A first draft is seldom your best work. But when revising, dodge two traps. Each will muddy the meaning. (1) Accuracy is a virtue. But science writers sometimes get nervous and overdo it. Don't keep on adding qualifications. Say it, let it go, and move on to the next sentence. (2) Brevity is a virtue too. But when you cut out too much, you end up being ambiguous. Example: "Patient care was and is a big part of the polio programme." That *patient* is ambiguous because the writer was cryptic. It would have cost only four letter spaces to begin: "Care of patients was . . ."

A Chinese proverb warns us, "It is useless to go to bed to save the light, if the result is twins."

4

NEW WORDS TO CONQUER

WRITERS in our field can count on readers who are waiting and eager. Whether they are laymen or specialists, human beings want to know about the new. They may or may not worship eternal truths, but they are entranced by the successive triumphs of technology and the changing concepts of pure science. It is therefore ironic that the new words of the technician cause so much trouble and, instead of holding readers, do much to drive them away.

Even if the neologism has been broken in a little, enough to be found in some dictionary, that isn't much help. The communications industry has become aware that people are in a hurry, would rather turn the page than turn to a dictionary. Highly trained technicians are different from other readers only in that if they find a treatise too difficult to read quickly, they file it away, hoping to give it another try sometime.

This chapter, about coinage, is the first of four dealing specifically with words. The next chapter deals with jargon, which is also a blatant troublemaker—but jargon words are not necessarily new. Then follow two chapters that dig deeper into our vocabulary needs. All four stress our obligation, which is to be clear, and deal with words that will give us the most for our time, our space and our desire to be known as literate.

There is a war of words, and the writer, any writer, takes sides. If he is alert, he wants precise words, not confused ones; working words, not weedy ones; powerful words, not puny ones. In short, good words, not bad.

Are new words always bad? Even a discouraged classicist would hardly claim that we suffered when *dephlogisticated air* became *oxygen*. Science needs new words because it works on frontiers.

It is understandable that the new words are painful to the layman. But why do they so often annoy the technician too?

It is well known that readers dislike "big words." Are the new words repulsive, then, because they are many-syllabled? Not necessarily. Let us compare *electroluminescence* and *id*.

The former describes a kind of lighting in which man imitates the firefly. Even if you haven't yet heard that we will be reading by the light of cold-glowing wall panels—no white-hot wires, no arcing discharge—the spliced word is not hideously complex. True, its seven syllables would give it a bad score if you applied the readability formula that places a premium on few syllables per word and few words per sentence. But the practical writer knows that the alternative would be to swap this one word for a string of shorter ones, and this, too, would come under the ban. Furthermore, when such lighting becomes common, the word will undoubtedly be shortened or given an easy trade name which will in turn become generic. Thus, a complex chemical became *nylon*, and another tongue-twisting plastic evolved, by way of *polyvinyl resin*, into *vinyl*. Meanwhile, the elements of the word for our new light are clearly visible. The meaning of *electro* is easy, and *luminescence* obviously has something to do with light. The reader who wants greater precision can then go to the dictionary and narrow down the meaning to the firefly kind of light.

Baffling *id*, on the other hand, shows how discouraging a short word can still be though it was coined more than 50 years ago. It is Freud's label for the amoral bundle of tendencies out of which develop our ego and libido. Science cannot measure this bundle, or even define it clearly. And the neologism itself gives no helpful clue. Even a biologist wouldn't see easily that *id* was clipped off his word *idioplasm*—itself jargonistic but carefully pointing back to its Greek origin.

Now *id* might be derided as another of those fuzzy words that oppress the social and pseudo sciences. But the technical sciences are vulnerable too. They cannot rely entirely on words describing equipment. They, too, must use words denoting concepts.

Take *sophisticated*. Here, to fill a need, engineering grasped an old word of the kind suspected by semantics and gave it a special, precise new meaning. This *sophisticated* may degenerate into a meaningless cliché like *fabulous*, but, until then, we have a neat and valuable tool. It was formerly merely an antonym of the Adam-and-Eve kind of simplicity. Reborn, it describes a mechanism that is highly complicated, and something more—it is highly refined too. And so we happily apply *sophisticated* to the "black-box magic" of a multispeed, gyro-steered, sun-powered telemetry system that rides a rocket to the moon and tells us what's happening en route.

Communications itself is another such "new" word—but it was accepted so quickly it never sounded novel. Formerly, it was limited to describing such activities as signalling. It now applies to the vast industry, composed of many media, that has multitudinous messages for our eyes and ears. All writing is communication. Furthermore, all writing—not only advertising and promotion—must be persuasive, if for no other reason than to keep the reader reading. Our own kind of writing is no exception. It differs only in emphasizing that the message must be clear.

Therefore our first commandment tells us: If this word won't work, find another. *Finnegans Wake* gives us words that are fascinating puzzles. James Thurber can upset us delightfully with the drawing that, he says, shows "a female Volt with all her Ergs in one Gasket." But science has to stick to precise meanings; the drumbeat of our writing must be clarity-clarity-clarity.

Clarity is also needed in the sentence. But troubles with punctuation, syntax and other elements of grammar cannot be solved until we take the muddiness out of words. The clearer they are, the better they can be cemented together. They are the building blocks.

Scholars—and less erudite people too—have long been fascinated by the mannerisms and mysteries found in words. Few remember Lewis Carroll as a mathematician; instead, we quote the upset clichés and jabberwockian words of his books about Alice. Isaac Newton considered his work in physics and mathematics less important than the time he spent mystically brooding on the meanings of words in the Bible.

Words, as words, are called constantly to our attention. Many books besides dictionaries deal entirely with the meanings of words. Lawyers pore over words; Patent Office examiners dissect them; TV programmes play with them. Teddy Roosevelt said, "Words to me are instruments." So were they to his famed contemporary William Jennings Bryan. Shakespeare made them sing—and also had Mark Antony rouse the rabble with them. Our Revolutionary War heroes made them ring, and inspired generations of patriots with "Give me liberty or give me death" and "In the name of Jehovah and the Continental Congress."

Such words and phrases may still suit science when it is evangelical, but in its workaday language it constantly requires new words. They may be coined in several ways, as we shall see. And a shorter new word is certainly handier than a long one. But always, clarity. How the word is coined is less important than what good or harm it will do. The average writer will rarely, if ever, coin a word himself. His main interest should be in knowing which new word to adopt, which to scorn—which, in other words, will give the reader help of some kind.

Science starts with some advantages when it coins words, because it works with patterns, analogies, derivations. Even the label-words *volt*, *angstrom*, *curie* stem from something meaningful —the names of noted scientists. Ot take the need for a word more specific than the unsatisfactory *heat*. You have known *thermometer* since childhood. The bridge to *thermal* is easily crossed in school. In college, spliced words begin tripping lightly off the tongue: *thermodynamics* is easy even if its concepts aren't, and *thermonuclear* neatly points to the H-bomb blast.

Now let's look at the other side—the ill-contrived, ill-derived, wild neologisms that do give trouble.

They are born the way they are because science is no longer

as staid or scholarly as it once was. Dean Dunning of the Columbia University School of Engineering says that "intellectually ambitious youngsters now often associate the term 'engineering' with crude grease-monkey work"; he wants more science taught to laymen, more nonscience taught to engineers. President Eric A. Walker of Pennsylvania State University warns that curricula are 50 years behind the times in their failure to give broader education to engineers. And the ranks of the technician are being diluted by an inrush of newcomers who want to cash in on the new fads, science and technology, quite willing to have fast education pass them along to specialized niches in fast production.

If all this is "scientism," to use a sneer-word coined on the liberal-arts side of the campus, it is not so sinister that it cannot be cured. Educators are trying new methods to improve both science and writing. Meanwhile, some orderliness in the lawless society of words is maintained by specialized groups such as the Nomenclature, Spelling and Pronunciation Committee of the American Chemical Society. But chemists are classifiers at heart. When they broke petroleum down into its constituents, they did it to the nice, orderly music of *methane, ethane, propane, butane* and so forth. From these come methyl alcohol, ethyl alcohol, propyl alcohol, etc.; now also, we have such plastics as polyethylene and polypropylene.

But too much coinage is catchword as catch can, and is giving us devilishly difficult words. Too often, adequate words are available but are passed by. The technician, especially if he is in the so-called glamour sciences, ignores them in favour of the fast-stepping bizarre words. And glamour leads him astray. When he tries to coin words the way Madison Avenue would do it, he is about as successful as a copy writer would be if he came into the laboratory to discover some mesons.

Two familiar types of coinage illustrate why our kind of writing is more successful when it sticks to common sense and clarity.

1. *George is a good word too.* Your product-planning team has designed and developed a new machine. It may not be proved out yet, but no matter. Like Ben Franklin, you can retort, "Of what use is a new-born babe?"

Now, what to name it?

Science is exploration. The reward comes when you feel like stout Balboa standing silent on a peak in Darien and discovering the Pacific.

This is fine. But restrain your exuberance. It can be as unwelcome as the unimaginative other extreme that made the black rat stagger under the learned trinomial *Rattus rattus rattus*. Remember that the new product will have to make its way in life.

More specifically, let's visit the world of computers. What's an Ace, or a Madam? These words are specially contrived acronyms. A step beyond merely abbreviating a phrase (*Works Progress Administration* became *WPA*), they are actual words formed from initials of other words. Ace, for instance, stands for Automatic Computing Engine—a subsequent model became Deuce. All this is name-calling by men who invent computers.

At the very least, the machines could all have the same identifying tag—as in Univac (Universal Automatic Computer)—by ending them with *ac*. This would describe them generically as automatic computers, which they are, rather than as logical engines and other nonsense. But even *ac* doesn't restrain exuberance.

Writing in *American Scientist*, Nelson Blachman relates how the wildness reached its zenith when several labs. tried to come out first with a new type of computer that could be called a maniac. Again the acronym was coined first, then words were assembled to justify it: *m*athematical *a*nalyser, *n*umerical *i*ntegrator *a*nd *c*alculator. There was even danger at one time that the maniacs would be generically called Johnniacs, after John von Neumann, who contributed much to their design.

The best that can be said for such naming is that the machines sometimes lead to end results that are somewhat in the same spirit. Some *maniacs*, for example, have been put to work solving problems that boil down to the advice given in those counterparts of the singing commercial, the singing weather forecasts:

> The sun today was hidden and won't say howdy,
> Because the forecast today is showers and cloudy.

The procession of flamboyant computers (*maniacs* were followed by *idiots* and *dafts*) finally led Argonne National Laboratory to name its new "brain" simply *George*. The letters mean nothing—they just add up to George. And James Reston of the New York *Times* has taken a fling at the nonsense, too, with his mythical *Uniquack*. It's the "brain" with which he satirizes the gobbledygook of Washington's bureaucracy.

If brand-new words often sacrifice clarity for sophomoric hilarity, so do older words receive sadly ambiguous new meanings. Thus, nuclear physics now has its *barn*. Here, the phrase "big as a barn" was stood upside down to define something spectacularly small—an area that is 10^{-24} square centimeters, big only in the sense that it has so many zeros after the decimal point. Far more sensible, even if slang was its mother, is the word that atomic-reactor workmen coined for the emergency that sends them racing to ram in the safety rods. It's a *scram*.

Ambiguity is also served by the new meaning that transistor people have given to *hole*. *Transistor* itself comes from *transfer-resistor*. It can be confused with nothing else. It exemplifies a competently telescoped "portmanteau" word. But *hole* is quantum-physics fantasy. We have to imagine an electron-size nothingness that moves through a crystal—now here, now there. Furthermore, we have to treat it as a material particle. But remember that there may also be genuine, drilled-in holes used for assembling transistorized equipment. Surely the genius that gave us magical transistors could have given confused engineers another word for make-believe nothingness.

Here, a bizarre word might have been well justified. For example, a British mathematician supplied *googol* to name the immensity of the numeral one followed by 100 zeros. Then came *googolplex*, which is the numeral one now followed by a googol of zeros. These particular two words, of course, exemplify something else—the "super-duper-wonderful" school of popularizing science. Most of us probably wouldn't need to use *googol* more often than once in a googol number of years, so why not stick to the neat superscript version, 10^{100}?

Ordinarily, the writer who wants to keep his reader will shun such brainstorming and remember simple clarity. He won't rush in to coin new words. If he needs one, he will follow models that stress clarity rather than cuteness or complexity.

Contrast the baffling acronyms of the computer world with

the quiet, ingenious *bit*. In its context it cannot be confused with another *bit*. Its size and meaning match the job it has to do. It's a telescoping of *binary digit*—the smallest bit of information that can be stored in a computer's memory.

Or contrast those acronyms with the new words for popular chemicals and drugs. These must start life with scientific names. Then word craftsmen go to work.

Sometimes, it's done with simple abbreviations, in much the way that governmental agencies became "alphabet soup"—FCC, OGPU, UNESCO. Thus, the farmer needn't struggle with *benzene hexachloride* (itself a condensation). He buys BHC. If he prefers another insecticide, he reads about the virtues of a substance known in chemical longhand as dichloro-diphenyl-trichloro-ethane. But what he reads is "DDT."

Other times, word-splicing does the job. When Lederle Laboratories came out with another of the antibiotics called mycins, this one became *aureomycin*—a gold-coloured product of mycology—and would have satisfied any etymologist. Similarly, *synthetic detergent* became *syndet*; more recently, *polymer fibre* has become *polyfibron* and the rocket fired from a balloon was christened a *rockoon*. Nor is there anything wrong with so-called "collision" words if they make sense. The simplest example is the pair of words that become one. After we have seen *missile* this and that frequently enough, the generic *missilecraft* becomes useful.

Contrast these products of coinage with a computer acronym like *mobidic*. This breeds inexcusable confusion. There is no connection with Moby Dick, with whaling. The *mobi* is from *mobile*.

In short, it is better to stick to the new noun that reveals what the gadget is made of, or who made it, or what it does, or the familiar word it came from.

2. Stop before you "finalize." Technician or not, the inexperienced writer is likely to be an imitator. This is good; it is part of the learning process. It can also be bad—when the writer borrows a new word for its glitter rather than for its clarity.

An example is the technician's fondness for "dynamic" words—for every *optimal*, *finalize* and *containerization*. These are like the new-name words in their weaknesses but unlike them in that they fasten on to qualities and concepts rather than new products.

These hash-words not only seduce the younger glamour science writers and those who work near the market place, but they are also infiltrating the staid sciences. They are alluring because they seem crisp and full of vitamins that can "beef up" weak prose. They are borrowed from the bad language of bureaucracy—big business and big government—and this is understandable. Both bureaucracies have been giving directives to science in recent years of hot and cold wars, and this association hasn't done science writing much good.

Imitate, yes. But it's disastrous to imitate the wrong model. For example, the souped-up words of magazines such as *Time* and *Variety*, suitable enough in their own fields, will make your technical report reel. Enjoy the nuances of *The New Yorker* but don't drag them into anything other than extremely offbeat advertising of new products. This same criterion of usefulness must guide your decision whether to borrow words like *ideation* and *definitize* from the bureaucrat's lingo.

Note again that we must face the facts of life. When good new words beat at the gate, we must admit them, even if classicists mourn. The Office of French Vocabulary has been crusading against words imported from America, but we take in new words because we need them—just as the French people have gone on importing *gangster*, *best-seller*, *pipeline*. It has long been thus. An Englishman got nowhere two centuries ago with his letter to the editor of the London *Chronicle:*

> When Physicians are at a loss to distinguish precisely the distemper that their Patients labour under, they have recourse to some appellation of which it is difficult to determine the exact meaning. Thus, we so often hear of *nervous* complaints, which were entirely unknown to our forefathers; and the sickness, which universally prevailed during the late unseasonable weather was distinguished by the pompous denomination of *the Influenza*. At a loss to account for the strange disorders which have infected this nation in its political capacity, I shall suppose it to have laboured under a most dangerous *Influenza*, an *Influenza* which has spread to the almost total destruction of the *Constitution*.

E

Influenza or not, Samuel Johnson needed only 58,000 words for his trail-blazing English dictionary. Much has happened since then. With its great gulps of plastics, transistors, radio echoers, satellites, medical terms, psychoscientific terms, marketing terms and so on, the language now totals well over a million words. It's expected to reach two million in the next hundred years. Not only new name-words but new concepts will swell the number.

We may escape that host of new-old words, the vocabulary of "Unthink," promised us in the book *Nineteen Eighty-Four* by George Orwell, but in science we are already becoming acquainted with the fantastic antimatter concept wherein nuclear particles like neutrons, protons and lambdas are being faced by their opposite numbers—the antineutrons, antiprotons, antilambdas.

All such new words say things that didn't need saying before, but do need saying now. The "dynamic" *finalizations*, by contrast, must be judged by whether they say something better.

One guide is the doctrine of common usage. A host of American writers have endorsed Ralph Waldo Emerson's view that "college and textbooks only copy the language which the field and the work-yard made"; they agree that letter-perfect English can often be drivel; that *lousy* was good enough for Shakespeare. And the slangy world of the sports page has given us such successful craftsmen as Ring Lardner, Damon Runyon, Paul Gallico.

Opposed to the usage advocates are those etymologists, classicists, schoolteachers and other custodians of the language who deplore what they call anarchy. These purists are not as eloquent as the champions of common usage and are often dismissed as fuddy-duddies, but they do teach us good writing manners.

Let's be practical in our approach. The invasion of "barbarian" neologisms is justified only if it brings needed fresh blood. The barbarism of the beatnik is not that of the lusty barbarian. If you use a word like *ideation*, which is distinguished only by its illiteracy, it is costly to your reputation. It is also expensive when it kills off a superior word. And if it turns clarity into muddiness, it's shocking extravagance.

Tear gas came from the mouths of the doughboys it frightened. *DDT* frankly announces that it is a contrivance. *Aureomycin* was grown from Latin and Greek roots that point to its meaning. But *containerization* is hopeless hash. It seems to mean putting things into containers. What it wants to mean is putting small containers into a large one.

Or take *finalize*, another borrowing from bureaucratese. It's a barbarian but not at all hairy-chested. Many synonyms say the same thing better. Even *polish off* or just *finish* are more precise. Henry Ford would have asked, "Why *finalize* the contract? Why not just *sign* it?"

The inborn weakness of such words is one reason so many of them lack staying power. Their glamour soon fades; they come in and go out as fast as hit tunes. Meanwhile, however, they were weeds suffocating capable words.

Worst are those that stay on despite their weakness. Let us examine *optimize* and *optimal:*

a. They seem to go back to *optimum*, which is Latin for *best*. But here confusion enters. We already have *optimistic* from *optimum;* and from *optimistic* we have a quite different *optimize*— this one means *to be optimistic* or *treat optimistically*.

b. And why the new *optimize* anyway? The dictionary already has *maximize*. Jeremy Bentham, the British founder of Utilitarianism, coined *maximize* long ago, along with other useful words such as *international. Maximize* means what the new *optimize* does. If the adjective *maximal* sounds embarrassingly literate, be just another guy and say "tops." In either case, what need for *optimal*? If your meaning is slightly defensive—"best possible under the circumstances"—then say so clearly.

c. Biggest objection: Neither *maximize* nor the new *optimize* is precise enough for technicians. "Tops" in what? Instead of either *maximal* or *optimal*, the effective writer will say *strongest*, or *highest*, or *hottest*, or *fastest*, depending on what he is rating. Let's repeat: his goal is to be not cute, not complex, but clear.

The New Words—Your Guide

We have seen that the society of words is uncomfortably lawless. Handling the new words requires experience, and judgement too. Neither experience nor judgement can be taught. But there are also the guideposts of common sense.

Here are the ones that will help when parturition comes upon you or when you face the more common problem of choosing among, or deciding whether or not to use, the new words that you are hearing and seeing.

1. Widen your vocabulary. The more time-tried words you know, as we will see later, the better you will understand what others write. In your own writing a bigger vocabulary lessens the need for such rubbery crutches as *optimize* and *minify*. To increase your stock of words, read more.

Read in your own speciality, of course, but not there alone. One editor suggests reading in a different specialized field each day of the week—in engineering one day; in medicine the next; and so on. But there is such a galaxy of specialities! And each is buried in the jargons that I describe in the next chapter. General reading is much better. It will also improve your writing style. But always beware of glitter words. I know a technical editor who jots new words into a pocket notebook. This is sensible. So is his reading of *The New Yorker*. However, the first word on his notebook's first page is "unhinged," which he found in a comic bit by S. J. Perelman. That was years ago, and this editor still hasn't had to describe anybody as unhinged.

2. Collect good neologisms. It does help to keep a file of useful words not yet in the dictionary. Thus, when you see tongue-twisting *magnetohydrodynamics* cut down to *hydromagnetics*, or when you spot a plausible newcomer like *avigation*, *avionics* or *astrionics*, jot it down and save it. Whether you can pronounce it or not isn't vital unless you want to be a public speaker too.

3. Resist troublemakers. When reading in your own field be brutal with writers who smother you with unfair words. Not everybody can or should be as patient as the reader who wrote to his magazine that he couldn't understand one of the advertisements, and went on to ask, "What is this accurator?" It's much easier to turn the page, or to throw away that magazine and patronize better wordshops. But if your need forces you to pursue the subject, then stubbornly question the writer or editor who failed in his job of communication.

4. Control that urge to coin. Let others be the daring innovators unless you're a professional writer. Most new words expire quickly.

Even word experts can't guarantee a safe birth. Linguists tried hard to coin such plausibilities as *professoress* and *Americaness*, and failed. Ambrose Bierce, a writer's writer, had his miscarriages too. He was bothered, at the turn of the century, by *airship* because it described both the balloon and aeroplane. He suggested the etymologically sensible *pondro* for a heavier-than-air machine and *levitar* for a lighter-than-air machine. He was able to get neither off the ground.

5. *Favour your own tongue.* Remember that the simpler words we call Anglo-Saxon fare better. H. L. Mencken had fun coining *ecdysiast* for strip-tease dancer, but despite its etymology and his publicizing it in the unabashed Mencken manner, the word got lost. Remember also that there is a neurotic affliction that reveals itself right within the word given to it—*zenoglossophilia*. This means a love for words of foreign origin. In their dictionary of the language of psychiatry, Horace and Ava English make merry with this *zeno* word and other examples of amateurishness and pretentiousness. Concerning *folie à deux*—insanity in pairs—they ask, "Why not double psychosis or even gruesome twosome?" Formic acid—both the chemical and the word—comes from ants (Latin *formica* means *ant*). So psychologists coined *formication*: "A sensation as of ants crawling on the skin." Concerning this example of bad taste, the Englishes comment: "Distinguish from 'ants in the pants.' "

6. *Are you being narrow?* Science is a collection of -ologies. There is always room for more. For example, Dr. John Paul Scott is a biologist who has probed into the hereditary and environmental reasons why animals, and humans, are aggressive. His is the pioneering field called sociobiology. It is a sensible word. Each of its two elements refers to an important field; each is quickly recognizable. But beware of dignifying every subspeciality as a science all its own. A physicist working with lenses need not and should not be a *lensologist*. When a biologist concentrates on digestive matters, why coin *gastrobiologist*? Such pinpointing is a nuisance to most readers. It is also too reminiscent of the humour that gave us *bugology* and the pomposity that gave us *ballroomology* as well as *cleaneteria* and *pantorium*. Bad slang, worse etymology.

7. Is the new word really better? Though he deals with Principles of Uncertainty, the physicist Heisenberg is quite clear in his writing. He boils down the findings of Planck and Einstein to a meticulous but simple definition of the past, present and future— and without using a single new word:

> The past is something we can know by observation; the future is where we can still, in principle, intervene in the course of events; and the present, we now know from modern physics, is actually a finite though small time interval between the two.

If a new word is needed, it will come as easily and inevitably as did *fallout* from nuclear explosions. It may even be a worthwhile "dynamic" word. *Dynamo* itself is worth examining. It has been running out of work to do; *dynamos* are disappearing because their direct current is being supplanted by alternating current from *generators*, *turbines* and other more useful machines. But we still have supercharged individuals called human dynamos. And one of them yet may invent a dynamorama movie screen.

8. Test the word this way. Whether you or someone else is the coiner, first ask yourself if the neologism is needed, then ask if it makes good sense. Truly dynamic words, for example, are valuable when they replace wordy phrases. Harking back to Bentham and his need for *maximize*, we can also congratulate whoever it was who fathered *automation*. It nicely took over the job of saying "making a machine run by itself." But the reader of a book on architecture will only be staggered by *wholeistic* and its inevitable child, *wholeisticability*.

9. If you drop the hyphen. Combining two words is also a coinage technique. But combine for a legitimate reason, not just for fun. Space-saving can be a sufficient reason if the combination is already well known; we can then run the words together: *fallout*, *nosecone*, *someday*, *downbeat*. Clarity is another justification. Some day I hope that *high school* will be conventionally written as one word *highschool*, while *grade school* remains two words. Why? I simply want to control the troublesome adjective *high*. Thus, "high school averages" can easily mean high averages in grade school, or in high school, or even in college. "High-school averages," with the hyphen, is safe but "highschool" would be simpler and everybody recognizes its meaning.

10. Again, resist. Don't indulge in extravagant or outlandish words just for the sake of bizarreness. Such words as *Kiwi, Jackass* and *Mad* at Los Alamos make one wonder what goes on at the space-age laboratories there. On the other hand, *atom-furnace* makes quick sense to anybody. Even *electroencephalography*, though long, makes sense enough to be taken apart with the aid of a dictionary if need be. We find that *encephalo* means the brain and *graphy* means describing. So we have a word that means analysis of electrical activity of the brain. This is carried further in the deftly written *Industrial Bulletin*, a publication of Arthur D. Little, Inc., to mean decoding "the code in the head."

In general, spend less time worrying about the new words and more on the misused older ones. New-word trouble is basically another version of "big-word" trouble. It indicates the same flaws: writing before you know exactly what you're talking about; or trying to dazzle the reader; or covering up weak phraseology; or simply forgetting that the language of science requires that the functional come ahead of the fancy. It gives us the American acronym *Spook*—not only noisy but empty of meaning. Dissect it and it stands for "Supervising Program Over Other Kinds."

5

THE ANSWERS TO JARGON

WE are all guilty, more or less, of writing jargon. We are all guilty, too, of complaining about other people's jargon while we tolerate it in our own writing. Sometimes it sneaks past our guard. At other times we drag it in to brandish our knowledge—or hide what we don't know.

With jargon, as with other types of obscurity, we can blame much but not all of the trouble on "big words." Jargon can be ingratiatingly simple. *Metals Progress* magazine offers these examples of the kinds of statements that occur in research reports, and in parentheses explains what they really mean:

While it has not been possible to provide definite answers to these questions . . . (The experiment didn't work out, but I figured I could at least get a publication out of it.)

Three of the samples were chosen for detailed study . . . (The results on the others didn't make sense and were ignored.)

It is suggested that . . . (I think.)

It is clear that much additional work will be required before a complete understanding . . . (I don't understand it.)

Correct within an order of magnitude . . . (Wrong.)

These are the tactics of dodging, a euphemistic word for dishonesty. But jargon varies—it can also be quite honest. Perhaps the saddest jargon of tongue or pen, and too common in the sciences, is that of the expositor who has meekly followed instructions.

For example, take a long breath and wade through this offering by a magazine:

> He explained that spatial vector electrocardiograph generalizes transfer impedance into a spatial continuum concept where it becomes representable as a spatial vector point function very useful in determining the sequence of the cardiac cycle temporally and spatially. An extension of this theory, involving a multiple loop feedback dipole synthesizer, makes it possible to compute automatically and instantaneously the optimal vectorial point dipole representation of the heart as a current source.

This is hardly friendly, attractive prose. Even banks have learned that it pays to come out of hiding—that big glass windows and open counters bring in customers.

One thing is clear. The writer shied away from trying to translate. He lifted jargon verbatim from a research report. And the scientist himself probably was not confused. He had substituted a rule for common sense—he was dutifully using "precise" words. Quite likely these words had meaning for him. But they are also an undiluted outpouring of "big words" that would repel even his fellow specialist. The pity of it is that many others—doctors, instrument makers, computer engineers—would probably find this report valuable if the scientist or writer had only let in some fresh air, some synonyms explaining that we have here a three-dimensional heart-tester that will give instantaneous answers when used with a computer.

Another example has much simpler words, but they are dressed in the garb of false humility:

> In 1941 (Vol. 2, p. 33) reviewer derived a formula for "Y." In reviewing reviewer's article, author (Vol. 2, p. 138) criticized reviewer's formula on the grounds that it gave infinite "Z." In a later review of reviewer's article . . .

And so on. This does not even have the doubtful virtue of supplying bizarre words for the crossword puzzler. The writer here was obeying a typical technical journal's warnings against the vulgarity of speaking in the first person. Result: a bewildering company of reviewers and authors that a simple "I" and "my" would have sorted out.

One more example, this time at the other extreme—trying to popularize but, in doing so, forsaking common sense. It's a publicity writer's announcement about some new industrial equipment. Jargon gives him a chance to play cutely with words and you, the reader, abruptly find yourself puzzling through a panegyric to "low, low switchgear." What have we here? you ask. Might there be some special meanings for *low*? Or is this a salesman screaming bargains? When "low" and lowest" become overworked by his competitors, he outpromises them with his "low, low prices." If you care to quarry deeper into the announcement, you discover that the first *low* refers to height of this equipment. It won't bump its head against the ceiling. The second *low* refers to low voltage. The equipment won't shock you.

Here, jargon was also standard ambiguity. Ordinarily, however, jargon is not so much the double meaning of two-faced ambiguity as the frustrating no meaning at all. It is the speciality word that, innocently or serving as intentional fog, floors or vexes the nonspecialist; it is the technical or secret vocabulary that slams the door on everybody who isn't a fellow lodge member.

This concealment, where the mission is "revealment," is a costly kind of writing. Everybody who writes has something he wants to tell or sell, and he wants to be read by more, rather than fewer, readers. Remember that even if you are not selling merchandise, you are selling your words—you are persuading the reader to read, and to continue reading. Even the fellow lodge member will flee as quickly as possible from the spatial-vector stuff quoted earlier.

Because it is so universal, like sin, jargon will always be with us, certainly in specialized writing. Much of the "dynamic" language of motivation research is jargon—the up-to-the-minute kind. And the "blameless" science, archæology, speaks of its peaceful digging in the tongues of yesteryear—again, jargon.

How, then, can we curb this costly nuisance? How can we let most of the wind out of our billowing wordage? How, also, can we avoid being forced into a grim choice between jargon and illiteracy, between a usefully broad vocabulary and a primitively simple one? "Basic English" has been as ineffectual as Esperanto in offering any practical answer.

Any control of jargon must consider these realities:

a. There is no sure cure. Jargon is a universal fault. Merely haranguing against it is too much like the sermons of Calvin Coolidge's preacher, who was merely "agin sin."

b. More than any other writing fault, jargon must first be recognized before we can consider remedies. In this chapter we will see that it is often the mote in the other fellow's eye (and he sees it in your eye too).

c. It speaks in many tongues. Alexander Woollcott, fond of such nostalgic words as *wraprascal* and *tippet*, was as guilty of jargon as the much criticized technican or the semanticist with his "science of non-elementalistic evaluation" that considers the "neuro-linguistic and neuro-semantic environments" of an individual.

d. Don't expect the reader to know what he can't find in his standard dictionary, to recognize *Screwdriver*, *Countdown* and *Marstini* as vodka drinks of the Space Age. He can't be consulting all the lexicons of slang and jargon, and even they are neither complete nor up-to-date enough.

e. What is jargon to one reader may not be to another. Jargon can be uttered nonsense or precise label-words that science needs. These words have invaded chemistry, for example, in waves: the coal-tar derivatives that came in after Germany's monopoly was ended by World War I; the petrochemicals leading to new polymers and therefore new plastics after World War II. These name-words are needed. The sin of jargon is not so much in using "big words" as in flaunting show-off words, on the one hand, and deliberately esoteric words, on the other.

f. Universal sin is not easily legislated out of existence. Some countries try outlawing prostitution; others prefer licensing as a control. Writing, of course, is traditionally lawless. In a word-game like Scrabble you are restrained from using *syzygy* because there are only two *y*'s in the entire set of player's tiles, but nothing can prevent a typewriter from rattling off many *y*'s and *syzygies*. With jargon, then, the only hope is in moderation. The less jargon, the better; to practice this moderation, the best control is self-control.

g. When in doubt, cling to the reader. He's your salvation as well as your judge. Decide who he is—to what extent he shares your vocabulary—and then use only the technical and jargon words that he can be expected to understand or to decode easily. It's as simple as that.

THE COMPANY YOU KEEP

You cannot swear off jargon effectively until you know just what it is. Otherwise you may think you are being asked to toss out culture and diction and learning. Also, we have seen that science does need its precise name-words. In our specialized age, the evolution from *insecticide* to *pesticide* and then *adulticide* makes some sense, too, even though *bug spray* would satisfy most readers.

An oddity about jargon is that it is so often condemned by practitioners of jargon. When writer A brandishes *existentialism*, writer B calls him *obfuscator*.

This blaming the other chap is common in science, and understandable when we realize that science is not so much a language as a phalanx of dialects. We now have writing by "computer engineers," "gyro engineers," "electronics generalists"; by "behavioural scientists," "human factors scientists" and even "human engineers." This only worsens what is bad enough already. A horticulturist and a physicist, both interested in radiation, complain that they cannot understand each other. And if the physicist happens to be a home gardener, he asks why the horticulturist gets lost in jargon instead of explaining why squash and pumpkin do not crossbreed. Moreover, if they are music-lovers, they share Debussy's disgust with the "fog of verbiage" under which music critics have buried Beethoven's Ninth Symphony.

Then, too, all the old-line sciences snigger at the tall talk that befogs writing in the "pseudo" and social sciences. Yet we know that both psychiatry and surgery, for example, have had to contend with impostors who learned the jargon and went ahead successfully to practice the profession.

Nevertheless, jeering at the other fellow has its value. When you learn to spot the other chap's jargon, you have taken the first step towards recognizing your own "parrot talk" and "baffle gab."

Jargon, of course, has many relatives. It stands midway between cant, which is first-degree murder of the language because it is deliberate, and the cliché, which is more often empty-headed meaninglessness. It was cant that made the author of *Tristram Shandy* choleric:

> Grant me patience, just Heaven!—Of all the cants which are canted in this canting world—though the cant of hypocrites may be the worst—the cant of criticism is the most tormenting!

Before science grew so big and voluble, philology and its subdivisions did most of the fretting about jargon and how to define it. On their tongues the word experts rolled the differences and similarities—jargon, lingo, argot, gibberish, and then the gobbledygook of bureaucracy and the weirdies of the rock-'n'-roll and beatnik clans. The experts generally saw close kinship between jargon and cant. This was unfair, because cant is often defined as the secret language of thieves and vagabonds. The jargonist is a thief only in the sense that he steals a reader's time. Nevertheless, it is manifest that jargon keeps rather bad company.

Sir Arthur Quiller-Couch derided "the Vanity Fair of jargon" and called it the doorstep to ambiguity. As another outspoken English scholar, Fowler, did later, he was flailing jargon in general rather than the technician's variety, and had fun linking it to prim prose—the elegance that substitutes "domicile" for "home," "perspiration" for "sweat," and "lady dog" for "bitch."

This, then, is the pretentious type of jargon. It betrays innocents into saying "between you and I" when "between you and me," though less ornate, happens to be correct.

But jargon is also the blah-blah of a politician who says he doesn't want higher taxes or a cabinet office when he actually does. Shortly after taking up his duties in Washington, a Secretary of Defence complained, "The language of legislation is spooky. I keep asking myself, 'What is it really saying?'"

Jargon is the bucolic affectation of the lorry driver who says "tarpolean" when he knows it's "tarpaulin"; the member-of-the-club badge worn by cavalrymen, including educated West Pointers, who disdained the rest of the world by calling themselves the "calvary"; the speech of the baggy-pants burlesque comedian who gets a laugh from the yokels by pronouncing "connoisseur" as "conna-sewer."

But jargon is also the language of the science student who outgrows dog Latin and plausible nonsense—in favour of a spanking new amusement that will set him and his classmates apart from the rest. After making you guess, in vain, he explains that

$$\ln\left[\lim_{z\to\infty}\left(1 + \frac{1}{z}\right)^z + (\sin^2 x + \cos^2 x) = \sum_{n=0}^{\infty} \frac{\cosh y \sqrt{1 - \tanh^2 y}}{2^n}\right.$$

is the scientific way to say: One plus one equals two. Contrast that contrived equation with the simplicity of Einstein's literally earth-shaking $e = mc^2$, which explains the power of a nuclear explosion.

Jargon can be the exhilarating slang of the barkers and midgets who work at carnivals. It can be the delightful nonsense (with pinpricks of meaning) of Lewis Carroll writing about Alice in Wonderland and of baseball's Casey Stengel testifying before a congressional committee.

But jargon can also be serious stuff—pomposity of the cultist and passwords of the secret-society member. The jingoist is usually a jargonist equipped with a flag-waving set of catchwords; and Communist jargon has irritants of its own. Where is the difference when you weigh: deviationism, dogmatism, fractionalism, reformism, sectarianism, revisionism? All these, C. L. Sulzberger wrote in the New York *Times*, were Moscow synonyms condemning Marshal Tito's independent-mindedness.

Capitalism has its jargon, too, and critics such as Thorstein Veblen have had a merry time at the expense of soothsaying economists by mimicking their language with deadpan derision.

Education, of course, has its own jargon. An example is from a teacher's report on her youthful pilgrim's progress:

He is adjusting well to his peer group and achieving to expectancy in skill subjects. But I'm afraid his growth in content subjects is blocked by his reluctance to get on with his developmental tasks.

(In other words, this lad is a good mixer, okay in the three R's but not much imagination.)

And the best jargon of all is the kind that can jeer at itself. Listen to this draughtsman. He is explaining in doggerel that, to show how much he knows, "I have marked all my lines/ With mysterious signs/ That Einstein could never decode," and he goes on:

Now my drawing is finished and printed,
And I'm proud of its hazy design,
For I know there'll be chaos and ulcers
When it finally comes out on the line.
And a feeling of pride starts a stirring inside,
As my tracing is filed on the shelf,
For my quest has been solved with a print so involved
That I can't even read it myself.

Now let us dig a little deeper, more clinically, into this matter of detecting other people's jargon so that we can better recognize our own. Here's a glimpse at the language of two quite different technical fields.

Example 1—architecture. Paintings, clothes and buildings have this in common: They sell themselves to us through our eyes —they are designed. The fashion designers and painters have their jargons, of course, but neither of these fields is closely related to science. Their jargons are not deadly, but merely those of aesthetics.

Architecture, on the other hand, does incorporate much applied science, such as the physics of load-bearing structures and the chemistry of materials. And in architecture the floodgates of jargon open wide.

One illustration was given in Chapter 3 (page 36)—the three decades that R. Buckminster Fuller had to wait before the world understood and paid tribute to his "Dymaxion Principle" and the "tensegrity" (tension plus integrity) incorporated into his fantastically strong geodesic domes. He had crusaded for "energetic-synergetic" geometry and the distribution of forces in lattices made up of tetrahedrons. He had not explained that the dome is an exquisite balancing of the forces that try to make it collapse and the forces that try to tear it asunder, that this is the trick with which you could build a sort of thick-skinned tent in which the tautness is built into the latticework of the skin—so that there is no need for a centre pole.

Another example shows how easy it is to note only the mote in the other fellow's eye. In a discussion of architectural jargon, a professor of architecture writes:

> The aspects of architecture embody so many factors that its defini-tion has become almost unintelligible. It encompasses sociology, biology, physiology, aesthetics, engineering, space, decoration, etc., to the extent that architects attempting to write about it invariably engage in such mixed jargons that it results in an incomprehensible babel.

He then goes on to explain himself in such terms as "emana-tion" of a drawing, "disbalance," "cumulative field of reference," "dynamic equilibrium" and "prosaic agglomeration."

Certainly even rhapsodizing by John Ruskin tells us much more:

> For indeed, the greatest glory of a building is not in its stone, not in its gold. Its glory is in its age, and in that deep sense of voiceful-ness, of stern watching, of mysterious sympathy . . . which we feel in walls that have long been washed by the passing waves of humanity.

Example 2—medicine. This field, of course, is rife with jargon, partly because its roots are in the witch-doctor mumbo-jumbo that considers *toxicosis* always better than *poisoning*. Partly, too, because of the morale-building approach that gives the patient some pink pills for imagined ills and holds back the crisp truth about serious ones. As long as the prescription is written correctly, the patient is probably as proud of long-word ills as of plebeian ones; the misunderstandings are no more fatal than that between the young husband and wife who slept separately one summer because polio experts had been warning that the disease is spread by "intimate contact between people." The young couple understood "intimate" only in the prim-prose sense.

It is likely that medicine's jargon is most harmful to the doctors themselves. A specialist said as he came away from a research symposium: "I had to listen so hard to the words that I didn't have a chance to grasp the idea." And colleagues admitted nodding off during the blessed dark moments when slides were shown.

Yet medical matters can be described clearly—as a medical researcher like Hans Zinsser, and other writers such as Sinclair Lewis and Arnold Zweig have so brilliantly demonstrated.

The following passage is from Aldous Huxley's *After Many a Summer Dies the Swan*. This is a novel, but Huxley is a walking encyclopedia of science as well as an extremely competent writer, and his science fiction is as disciplined as any research report. In this passage, disregard his "style"; instead, note the expositional clarity—how words that might be jargon are quickly unfolded for you. At the beginning you know little about carp and probably less about the sterols; at the end you are ready to live as long as Methuselah:

Those sterols! (Dr. Obispo frowned and shook his head over them.) Always linked up with senility. The most obvious case, of course, was cholesterol. A senile animal might be defined as one with an accumulation of cholesterol in the walls of the arteries. . . . But then cholesterol was only one of the sterols. They were a closely related group, those fatty alcohols. . . . In other words, cancer might be regarded, in a final analysis, as a symptom of sterol-poisoning. He himself would go even further and say that such sterol-poisoning was responsible for the entire degenerative process of senescence in man and the other animals. What nobody had done hitherto was to look into the part played by fatty alcohols in the life of such animals as carp. That was the work he had been doing for the last year. His researches had convinced him of three things: first, that the fatty alcohols in carp did not accumulate in excessive quantity; second, that they did not undergo transformation into the more poisonous sterols; and third, that both of these immunities were due to the peculiar nature of the carp's intestinal flora. What a

F

flora! . . . In one way or another, in combination or in isolation, these organisms contrived to keep the fish's sterols from turning into poisons. That was why a carp could live a couple of hundred years and show no signs of senility.

Less Jargon—Your Guide

Now let's focus on your own writing. You think you can recognize jargon. You want to cut it out of your sentences and paragraphs, or at least cut it down. But how?

1. Preventives come first. Beware of infection by the other person's jargon and you will save time on cures. Here are some ways to avoid infection.

a. Don't parrot the instructor's bigger words. They may get you a college degree, but professional life requires writing that is more than regurgitation. Jargon, for example, doesn't impress a capable boss. He's too busy, and wants to pick your brains in a hurry. He doesn't equate complex writing with complex thoughts and, in fact, is suspicious of thoughts that cannot be simplified.

b. Spurn the words that bother you in your reading—they may bother your own readers. For example, just as too many isms, each requiring its own political party, can paralyze the functioning of a government, so can the spinning off of too many -ologies throw our language into bedlam. Let metaphysics insist on its ontology, but need our writing stagger under all these: behaviouristic psychology, Gestalt psychology, normic psychology, structural psychology, functional psychology, act psychology, dynamic psychology, reflexological psychology?

c. If you are editing or rewriting the work of others, translate the jargon when you can; when you can't, call for something simpler from the author. Otherwise, you are an accessory after the fact. As editors know, this can lead to troublesome bickering. The best cure is to let the author take his jargon elsewhere. Of course, before you challenge fact or jargon, be sure of your ground. A garbage grinder, for example, may prefer the sweet smell of another name. A magazine editor learned this from a plaintive letter sent in by a manufacturer:

We prefer that you call it correctly as "Industrial Disposal Unit." Garbage grinder connotes shoddy appearance, etc. Certainly, any machine capable of disposing of "Top Secret" documents should not be called a garbage grinder.

2. Who's your reader? Delay writing until you have decided who the reader, or class of readers, will be. If you don't know, you are still too hazy about the subject itself.

Is it to be a proposal to the boss? That isn't identification enough. Is he strictly a management man, does he have a smattering of science, is he a fellow technician? Or is it to be a pass-along proposal that will be read by all three types of person?

If your paper is for fellow specialists, the jargon content can go up. But again, remember that people in promotion and advertising may have to read it, too, and they cannot translate what they cannot understand.

If you are writing for a magazine, who are its readers? If for students, are they at graduate or freshman level? And what of the so-called general public? It turns thumbs down quickly even on a literate writer if he strays too far from words like *home* and *income*.

When picturing the audience, remember: (a) Clarity brings its own reward—the less jargon, the wider the potential readership; (b) if you really prefer a narrower audience, don't be misled by specialization. Writing for "farmers" isn't narrow enough—the applegrower has one lingo, the poultryman another. Similarly, your comrade technician isn't your twin in training and interests.

3. Simplification isn't that simple. Don't let the preaching against jargon panic you into such lisping simplicity as "A river pump house pumps water to the water treatment plant" and "He was a self-educated man educated by himself."

And by all means don't be panicked into popularization that falls on its face. When the United States Weather Bureau introduced its Discomfort Index, that term was simplicity itself compared with the attempt by a newspaper to explain it:

. . . The relationship between such variables is found by computing a third measure. This is a magnitude so related to the magnitudes of temperature and humidity that to values of these measures there correspond values of the third measure. This third measure is called a function, a measure of relationship. . . .

4. If you don't know, say so. Is your chain of facts secure? If links are missing, you have this choice: (a) Ignore the gaps—but this leaves you open to being called slipshod, or worse; (b) delay the final draft until you can supply the missing facts, or bypass the trouble area and limit your writing to what you do know about; (c) come right out and say "I don't know." Truly great scientists frequently exhibit such humility. It can also be very refreshing. Thus, in a nonpompous article in *Scientific American*, Robert T. Wilson, the physicist, discusses Soviet particle-accelerators:

> Veksler . . . envisages a small bunch of ions in a plasma. . . . These waves are to act together coherently to give an enormous push to the ions being accelerated. If this is not clear to the reader, it is because it is not clear to me. The details have managed to escape most of us because of a linguistic ferrous curtain, but Veksler speaks of the theoretical possibility of attaining energies up to 1,000 bev. . . .

5. Ordinary words are respectable. Don't let very simple words cause you shame. Note that Wilson, above, used *bunch*. Other topnotch technicians are similarly unafraid of writing like human beings. If nuclear writing can be handled this way, why not that of the applied sciences? For example, medicine—which concerns everybody—might well emulate agricultural science, which also deals with quite ordinary people. Agronomy, horticulture, animal genetics—these have ponderous jargons of their own. But listen to the homely language of a typical county agent talking to his farm flock over the radio, or read the yearbooks issued by the United States Department of Agriculture. Some of the most capable writing by experts and editing by experts can be found in these technical annuals. The researchers in agriculture, fighting the gloomy predictions of Malthus, learned long ago to clarify their writing or let others do it for them; that a discovery is incomplete until fellow technicians, and eventually the farmers, can apply it.

6. Common cure—a synonym. Whenever you suspect jargon is creeping in, call on substitute words that are easier. (The next two chapters will discuss truly simple words and, especially, the precise ones needed in science writing.) In general, simplicity of the word should depend on simplicity of the reader. New York's radio station WNYC, addressing all kinds of people, was smart enough to use "the coming bookkeeping year" instead of "fiscal year"; this avoided confusion in listeners' minds between fiscal and calendar years. Experts, too, are grateful for simpler words, for each time the chemist says "nylon" instead of giving the full molecular name of the polyamide.

7. But some jargon is necessary? If so, rush in to explain it to the reader. This can be done in several ways. A shortcut method is the parenthetical one. Be quite formal, use jargon if you must, but immediately define the word. The New York *Times* does this frequently and nicely, with the synonymous material flanked by parentheses or dashes. Thus:

> The volume, amounting to 417 lots (50,000 pounds to a lot) was the second highest this year.

> The metal is as light as magnesium alloys, yet its modulus of elasticity—or stiffness—is about three and one-half times that of steel.

The same method works handily when writing for a more technical audience. Thus, from the Beckman Instrument Company, an announcement about its D2 Oxygen Analyzer says:

> . . . Oxygen is unique among gases in being strongly paramagnetic (attracted into a magnetic field). Other gases are, with few exceptions, slightly diamagnetic (repelled out of a magnetic field). . . .

Obviously, to be effective, the explanation must explain. In the following, from *Scientific American*, the reader either understands or doesn't understand precisely what is meant—the explanation (which I italicize) merely adds bothersome words:

> The rate of change of the orbital period of a satellite, *that is, the rate of change in the time it takes to fly its orbit*, is directly proportional to the density of the atmosphere through which it passes.

8. Comparisons are practical. Another effective way to make jargon more palatable is to put similarity to work. An

example is the "For example . . ." method so useful in all expositional writing.

For example, the atom was formerly likened to an infinitesi-
mally tiny billiard ball—a hard little atom. But later, when the
concept was revised to include spinning electrons, the student was
asked to think of a tiny planetary system.

Or take mathematics—almost as much of a terror to most technicians as it is to laymen. A mathematician with a new concept
about finite groups was asked by a newspaper reporter to explain
it. His first answer was that this could not be done simply enough
for the layman. But he then did it very effectively in terms of
wallpaper patterns.

This method, however, requires considerable caution and common sense. The horrors of a mixed metaphor must be avoided. The
analogy must be sharply to the point—or the reader's mind is sent
wandering off the subject. And it's hardly helpful to have the
mitosis of a human's cells likened to the mitosis of a guinea pig's
cells—if the reader doesn't know what mitosis means.

Allow the example to be lengthy only if it is itself an integral
part of the exposition. And don't reduce the reader's mental stature
to that of a child. A New York *Times* story, in the course of reporting
a speech by a university president, quoted this sentence, "Today,
our specialists, as they study man and his behavior, are all too
frequently like the blind men studying the elephant." At this point
the reporter, evidently disbelieving that *Times* readers are fairly
literate, launched into a parenthetical paragraph of 85 words that
retold the familiar blind-men-and-elephant story.

9. This is the smoothest way. The good craftsman, like
Aldous Huxley, quoted earlier, can have his cake and eat it too. He
throws in troublesome words when necessary but quickly explains
them with what might be called built-in paraphrasing, which
advances the exposition while explaining the jargon. Difficult word
and explanation come so closely together that the reader feels no
pain, hardly realizes what has been done for him.

Let us work through a step-by-step example. The problem I
am about to describe actually exists. Some day it may be solved. I
am imagining that day has arrived and I want to announce the

triumph. If I were writing a typical research paper, I would begin something like this:

> The literature contains many references to a problem that has been important in silviculture for the last fifty years. . . .

And so on, until I come in pages later with what it is I want to announce.

An unappetizing beginning? Yes. But clarity is our main concern here. Focus on the word *silviculture*. How many readers can I assume would have a roughish idea of its meaning? Worse, how many would know its precise meaning? Very well then, I can conquer jargon this way:

> The literature contains references to a problem that has been important in silviculture for the last fifty years. Silviculture is defined as the art of producing and caring for a forest. . . .

With this interruption for definition I have obeyed the injunction to explain any jargon. But at considerable expense. The unappetizing beginning has become even more deadly, and I have wasted space just to give a definition.

Yet this *silviculture* is a word I really want to use throughout the article; I also believe sincerely that if the reader doesn't know the word, it's high time he learn it.

Now let's try the technique of paraphrasing. If I insist on beginning with a review of the literature, this will at least purge the jargon (the difficult word and the explaining words are in italics):

> The literature contains many references to a *forest-growing* problem that has been important in *silviculture* for the last fifty years. . . .

Or, the same, but with dullness thrown away:

> Science is now certain that the American chestnut *tree* can be brought back into our *forests*. Government *silviculturists* are successfully *growing thousands of* chestnut *seedlings*. These are identical in species with the towering trees that perished when a mysterious blight began attacking them fifty years ago. . . .

Or, the same, extremely popularized:

The deadliest killer of America's *trees* has now been licked. Fifty years ago, *silviculturists* watched helplessly as a mysterious blight swept across the country, turning *forests* of lordly chestnut trees into companies of grey ghosts. Five years ago, science found in coal tar a chemical that was just as deadly against the blight. A month ago, *silviculturists* of another generation jubilantly began *planting new forests* of chestnuts. . . .

Or, very simply, merely telling somebody about something I do on my farm:

I like *silviculture. Growing forest trees* is more than a hobby with me.

Here, I have had different audiences in mind but the method is always the same. I define the word as I move along.

Another example. I cannot assume that all readers of this book are steeped in the jargons of grammar and semantics. But I do assume that most of you have had a college education or will have. Therefore I feel no need to define such words as *antecedent* and *adjective*. But in the chapter on new words I was much more doubtful about *neologism*. Yet I felt you should know this word. So I hastily defined it, not by pedantically saying, "A neologism is . . ." but by letting the act of definition do some other work for me. I had been discussing new words. Then I went on, "Even if the neologism has been broken in a little, enough to be found in some dictionary . . ."

All of the preceding methods can be lumped together as follows: Don't expect the reader to supply the explanation. He's too busy or doesn't know how. If you cannot explain, change the subject, or aim for another kind of reader.

While I was at lunch one day with some visiting engineers from the USSR, the conversation turned to translations. I asked if these foreigners had read Vance Packard's *The Status Seekers*. They said they expected to—the book was being translated into Russian. And what about *The Hucksters*? I asked. They nodded with comprehension—yes, they had heard about it. But, they added, it wouldn't be translated into Russian. Why? Their answer was convincing. The USSR had status-seekers too—so the Packard book would make sense. But the concept of free-enterprise advertising, of huckstering, defied translation into terms that Russians could understand. So Frederic Wakeman's book on hucksters would be jargon—to Russian readers. And why publish jargon?

6

SIMPLE WORDS — HOW SIMPLE?

THE language of science is distinguished by its abundance of new words. Otherwise, it shares vocabulary problems with other expositional writing. Its individual words talk too much— are longer than necessary; its lazy phrases, like "in the last analysis" and "from the standpoint of," add up to so much verbiage.

The result is that the technician, like other writers, finds it easy to say in two pages what could better be said in one. That he can be so wordy, and still be baffling, is his peculiar affliction.

This chapter deals with overlong words in general. Why condemn only jargon? Even more insidious are such words as *alleviate* when *ease* or *lessen* would do, *tabulation* when *table* or *list* would do.

Writers are constantly urged to be concise. This is not enough. Brevity, yes, but how brief? Too often forgetting that clarity is the main goal, the inexperienced writer sacrifices words and becomes cryptic. The skilled writer, by contrast, practices pragmatism. He knows how helpful it is to save space here so that needed words can be added there.

Another common injunction is: Be simple. Yes, but how simple—and still remain accurate and literate? Writers like Walt Whitman, Bret Harte and Mark Twain all had the same superb teacher, the old-fashioned printing press. As printers' apprentices who set type by hand, they learned to favour the shorter words that meant less work. This training stayed with them. Though they later became fluent, their writing remained lean—and strong.

But we no longer receive such training. Furthermore, those writers were not chronicling the progress of science, whose vocabulary contains so many speciality words.

Our kind of writing needs something more practical than the unworldly commands Be brief; Be simple. That is why I end this chapter with a list of words, both technical and nontechnical, that the alert editor regards with suspicion. He pounces all the more quickly on these overgrown words when they merely dull the meaning. Check through the list to see how many appear too often in your own writing—and note the serviceable replacements for them.

The list cannot, of course, be followed blindly. Words must be weighed—for fatness, for triteness and, in our writing certainly, for content. This takes judgement. And judgement is acquired, not taught. But it is acquired faster when you have models to follow, and examples showing what to avoid. Let's look for such additional guidance.

THE 4-LETTER APPROACH

When two words say the same thing, the choice is simplified. You judge them by their length. The shorter is preferable. When they are not exactly synonymous, you can get into trouble. This is why, in science writing, or almost any other kind, the quick formula for readability—the fewer letters, the better—is suspect. This is simplifying that is too simple. But as long as we hold on to common sense, as long as we keep sight of the fact that *cold* isn't the same as the longer *frigid* and the latter isn't the same as the still longer *refrigerated*, the technique gives us a handy gauge.

It can even be fun. Frank Gellett Burgess, the American humorist and illustrator best known for his jingle about the purple cow, wrote an entire article, "What's Wrong with Four-letter Words?" in words of only one syllable. His feat begins, "This is a plea for the use of more short words in our talk and in what we write." It ends, "Short words are words of might."

Such stunts, however, are less worthwhile than the way Charles F. Kettering put shorter words to technological work. When he endowed a research foundation at Antioch College, he did not say his goal was to isolate, analyze and synthesize the chlorophyll molecule. To reach the general public, he simply said, "We want to find out why grass is green."

Similarly, describing his own pioneering with the automobile self-starter and the two-cycle diesel engine, he spurned the languages of both high-flown science and motivation research. He said, "The inventor fails 9,999 times and if he succeeds once, he is in."

Many others have glorified the shorter word, in practice and in preachment. Quiller-Couch mocked "elegant writing" by pumping pomposity into Hamlet's soliloquy. His paraphrase began: "To be, or the contrary" and ended "and thus a consummation achieved of a most gratifying nature." Another parodist is J. B. McGreachy, Canada's popular commentator on the arts. He derides "genteelism" by showing how its aversion to the simple word *sweat* would destroy the beauty of a line from the Bible: "In the perspiration of thy face shalt thou eat bread." He goes on to show that Basic English, on the other hand, is no better, because it would convert Winston Churchill's ringing defiance into "blood, face-water and eye-water."

Call it genteelism in other literature, or pomposity in science writing—it's much the same thing. It does not heed the old adage that tells us important things come in small packages. The names of such magazines as *Time*, *Life*, *Look* show the value of sticking to four-letter words. When Goethe wrote in his *Faust* "When ideas fail, words come in very handy," he was scorning the same big words that a modern advertising executive, Arthur Kudner, had in mind when he wrote this advice to his son:

> *Never fear little words.*
> *Big long words name little things.*
> *All big things have little names*
> *Such as life and death, peace and war*
> *Or dawn, day, night, hope, love, home.*
> *Learn to use little words in a big way.*
> *It is hard to do*

But they say what you mean.
When you don't know what you mean—
Use big words.
They often fool little people.

And if a photograph can be worth a thousand words, then the reverse is true too. A thousand pictures could not have equalled the defiant word "Nuts!" with which General Anthony McAuliffe answered the Nazi demand that he surrender at Bastogne.

But do science writers have their special problems? Must they remember the difference between *cold* and *refrigerated*? Agreed. In our search for guidance, then, a good starting point might be one of the "Ten Commandments" that the Minneapolis-Honeywell Regulator Company issues to its technical writers. This injunction says: Thou shalt not show off thy technical vocabulary. Good—but it does not go far enough. It should state: Thou shalt not show off thy vocabulary.

The technician who is too wordy in his profession is also a show-off out of it. The two faults are one. I have sometimes asked students to write on subjects outside their special interest in science. There was no difference. Those who were long-word lovers still wrecked their prose with words they had no business trying to use. They wrote such phrases as: "our psychologically oriented age"; "I want to alienate any confusion"; "I was made cognizant"; "he is quite effective in immuning against comprehension"; "I learned this slightly hieroglyphical thing"; "invoking the implementation."

Otherwise, the commandment is good because it forbids only overcomplexity. It does not banish the leeway we need when our writing has to go beyond *nuts* and *bolts*. For example, *perpendicular* is two syllables and five letters longer than *vertical* but is often superior because it covers more ground. It is not limited to describing something that is upright. Similarly, until a good substitute comes along, we will have to keep the longish word *technology*.

The trouble is not only with "big words." We have seen that jargon can be monosyllabic; so can such glistening renovations, fresh from the lab., as *barn* and *hole*. Or take the show-off *lox*. It looks simple enough—so simple that you think of delicatessen fish and overlook the Space Age meaning—a liquid-oxygen explosive that gives zip to a rocket. *Lix* or *loxy* would have been as breezy without introducing ambiguity.

The show-off word and a simple version may be equally bad. For some reason, technicians like to write *magnitude* when *size* would suffice. Often, neither is precise enough. Then why not the simpler of the two? If neither the exalted word *ebullition* nor the commonplace *boiling* is specific enough, why not the latter? You can at least modify it and make it *boiling over*.

THE ART OF BEING SIMPLE

It is easy enough to throw away a nonsense phrase like *accounted for by the fact that* or chop it down to *because*. The typical "big word" needs more delicate handling.

Suppose you want to escape from *contiguous to*. Then you need a synonym. But *contiguous*, besides being ponderous, is defective because it has several meanings. Shall the synonym be *next to*, *near*, or *touching*? You must first examine just what it is you mean.

Or suppose you want to simplify the shorter but nonetheless overstuffed word *factor*. It has become so imbedded in our language that you cannot think of a suitable synonym. Then why not recast the sentence and get right to the point?

> *Stuffed:* This chemical has a factor that is partially responsible for the ability of hogs to convert wastes into pork.

> *Simple:* This chemical helps hogs convert wastes into pork. (*Then go on with what the chemical contains, if you know.*)

Call on synonyms. Recast sentences. Those are two of the best ways to simplify. But devices aren't enough. You must first be aware of the need to simplify.

Examine yourself. Do you go on writing difficult prose because of habit? Or is it because you fear that simpler words would seem unprofessional, undignified, uneducated or whatever? If so, you should realize that the word *simple* isn't that simple. In our context, it has no kinship with *foolish* or *ignorant*. Instead, Be Simple is another way of saying Be Natural. And there we have a respectable, time-honoured prescription for effective writing.

It brings results. Fewer nuisance words means your fellow scientists will be more eager to give time to your research paper, the magazine editor will be more interested in your article or new-product announcement, the chief engineer will be more receptive to your recommendations, and so on down to the personnel manager who will be more willing to read your job résumé.

Very well then, how to be natural? Rule books can't tell how. Willa Cather came close to the answer: "It takes a great deal of experience to become natural."

This need not be frightening. A big element in experience is discarding what "ain't so." It's not true that you are being helped by such overstuffed words as *disseminate, criterion* and all their brethren who talk too much while saying too little. Reject them and the rest is much easier. You can then equate effective simplicity with skilled craftsmanship. And craftsmanship, we all know, is learnable.

In other words, we begin to look on writing as an art. And it is a truism that really great art is simple. It has to be, to get down to the big truths.

For example, compare your writing with the kind that great music has found useful for libretto purposes. And consider how well such music is in tune with the simplicity of the words. The "Domine Deus, Rex Coelestis" in Vivaldi's *Gloria* might have been a complex, thunderous chorus. Instead, it is sung by a solitary woman's voice—one frail human praising her God. The other masters knew this powerful device too. Bach had his "Sheep May Safely Graze" type of pastorale, and so did Handel. Though *The Messiah* is florid baroque, it did not, as originally written, allow hundreds of voices in the chorus—Handel wanted his little concertino orchestra to be heard. Nor does this oratorio crash with Hallelujah throughout. For the words that his librettist selected from the King James Bible, Handel supplied the heart-rending simplicity of a lone contralto singing "He shall feed his flock like a shepherd," and the radiance of a chorus that matched music and the words "His yoke is easy; his burthen is light."

To the nonparticipant, all this seems only natural. Just write the way you talk—or the way Rembrandt simply slanted a beam of light down on his subject. The simplicity of Rembrandt wasn't quite that simple; *The Messiah* wasn't the prattle of babes. Artistry was at work, bringing grandeur down to earth, making the complex seem simple.

Geniuses are few, but many people can become competent. Naturalism in writing is learnable. It is a skill that the writer acquires, just as the athlete learns his speciality—how to vault or to box in a way that looks easy. Skiing didn't teach me choral singing and choral singing didn't teach me how to ski, but the learning process was the same and so was the goal. You don't see awkward strain in an Olympics skier swooping down the mountain any more than you do in Marian Anderson when she sings an emotional spiritual. The competent writer, too, makes his art look easy. He eliminates the needlessly complex words.

The learning process is accelerated when you examine the smooth writing of experts. Reading good prose can help lighten your own—and no learning method, of course, is more entertaining. This is what nontechnicians call, a bit inaccurately, learning by osmosis. It cannot work wonders, will not substitute for learning through trial and error. But it will at least dispel any lingering fear that you degrade yourself by writing in a fashion that is easily understood.

Einstein did not hesitate to come out of the fourth dimension and explain his energy-equivalence equation in terms of splitting an atom, which he likens to a rich miser. When this atom dies—is split by fission—its two offspring cannot quite inherit all of the property. Some has to be left to the community:

> This part, though relatively small, is still so enormously large, considered as kinetic energy, that it brings with it a great threat of evil. Averting that threat has become the most urgent problem of our time.

It is better, of course, to read the writers who make a speciality of popularization. Some of their naturalness will rub off on to you and relax your muscles. The growing interest in science has resulted in anthologies that have the advantage of offering several such writers in one volume. For example, the same volume that has

Rachel Carson writing about the sea may also take you back to Jean Henri Fabre, the physicist who turned entomologist and wrote, in words no more complex than need be, of:

> . . . the beetles whose proud mission it is to purge the soil of its filth. . . . The Spanish Copris carries on his forehead a powerful pointed horn, curved backwards, like the long blade of a mattock. . . . The Lunary Copris has two strong spikes, curved like a plough-share, springing from the thorax. . . . All are supplied with a shovel, that is to say they have a broad, flat head with a sharp edge; all use a rake, that is to say they collect materials with their toothed forelegs.

You will also find good popularizers today writing for newspapers and magazines. They, in turn, have modelled themselves after the pioneering science editor of the New York *Times*, Waldemar Kaempffert. Technical terms didn't daunt him—or his readers. The big words of science entered his articles in friendly fashion, then moved quietly out of the way.

If you have time to read only in the technology field, you can find a wide variety of models, ranging from articles in *Fortune* to the books in which Roger Burlingame describes how mechanization has come upon us. Or note how successfully the *Wall Street Journal* simplifies the jargons of economics and technology. It has earned praise for being the newspaper with the most readable first page in the nation.

Or read those engineering magazines that have learned this: You must first woo the reader if you want to woo the advertiser. These journals make sure that their articles begin at least in such fashion that any technician, whatever his speciality, will not get lost. Here's an example of an opening paragraph:

> The failure diagram offered by the author is another step in the direction of getting more out of metals. It gives you a better picture of the risks that you can take—and the safety factors governing them—when stresses are caused by a complex pattern of loads. It applies to all materials whose ductility characteristics are similar to those of steel.

Let's turn now to a paper that was presented at the meeting of an engineering society. It arouses my interest because it is

G

noticeably a good try at effective writing. Its title is nicely persuasive, "Why Hate High Pressure Pneumatics?" This is so forthright and simple that I can ignore the absence of a hyphen needed between *High* and *Pressure*. The rest of the paper is sometimes shaky in its punctuation. That, too, can be forgiven because I am interested here in something else. In the following passage, I have smoothed the punctuation. Otherwise, it stands as it was written. Note how the paper begins, with easy sentences and easy words:

> We all have our likes and dislikes in life. Many times, our feelings are based on incidents that occurred early in our education or training. The trouble is, we do not usually take the time to evaluate changes and advancements which might alter our opinions.
>
> At one time I disliked high-pressure pneumatics for the same reasons that many of you here today dislike the system. High-pressure pneumatic systems, I thought, were too dangerous, too complicated, and too heavy.
>
> Now, after design and field experience, I favor high-pressure pneumatics for some systems, and I would like to point out why I do. . . .

It then goes on to sonic speeds, to the bursting pressures in car tyres and in high-flying aeroplanes. Conspicuous by their absence are such padded words as *fundamentally* and *essentially*. True, the cryptic "after design and field experience" should be recast into "after experience with design and in the field." Elsewhere, tight editing would squeeze out needless water. For example, throw out the entire first paragraph and you have the craftsmanlike type of beginning I discuss in Chapter 11.

What I am stressing here is that this writer has high potential. He has already conquered the worst disease of the beginner. He dares use simple words and reject pompous ones.

Simplification need not be limited to writing about "hardware." Suppose your exposition takes you into complexities of "pure" science. Physics, for instance, not only ranges through subspecialities like astrophysics and nucleonics; it also dips into philosophy. Listen to Arthur S. Eddington explaining that the theory of probabilities has weakened determinism and restored hope in free will, and note that he doesn't bog us down in the horror words of metaphysics:

> How can we be responsible for our own good or evil nature? We feel that we can to some extent change our nature; we can reform or deteriorate. But is not the reforming or deteriorating impulse also in our nature? Or, if it is not in us, how can we be responsible for it? I will not add to the many discussions of this difficulty, for I have no solution to suggest. I will only say that I cannot accept as satisfactory the solution sometimes offered, that responsibility is a self-contradictory illusion. The solution does not seem to fit the data.

If you still fear that physics cannot be simplified, then read this from the well-written textbook that taught me college physics:

> Electrons will not stand much crowding. Electricity is, in fact, about the most incompressible stuff that we know of. If the least bit of it is forced into a conductor at one place, the same amount must come out somewhere else.

This was hardly fearsome prose. It led deeper into the behaviour of electrons, but it never forgot the successful writer's formula: Remember the reader.

True, that book was designed to be instructive. But all of our kind of writing is intended, one way or another, to be instructive. Furthermore, that book is not representative of all texts in our field. A large number are notoriously more difficult than need be. They are repositories of bad writing.

The failure to write simply is most glaring, of course, when it occurs in writing that urges simplicity. Let's look at a specialized instruction book—this one on how to write technical reports. Its first chapter contains the usual injunction:

> "Fine Writing" and uncommon or "high-sounding" words or phrases are out of place . . . and should be avoided.

Yet that chapter is titled "Emphasis on Empathy." Now *empathy*, like *serendipity*, can be useful—or merely a high-sounding word. And like *serendipity* it is more often used incorrectly than correctly. Furthermore, the chapter is devoted entirely to simple facts on card filing, typing, grammar. There is nothing in it about empathy. The word is not even mentioned. Here, then, is a word used in a show-off way that violated a first principle—the title should not baffle the reader, should have some relation to the text.

The title of this chapter is: "Simple Words—How Simple?" The answer is indicated in the title and examined in the discussion. The answer is not a dictum: Use simple words. The answer adds up to: *Prefer* simple words: *favour* simple words. Those are the verbs that will guide the practical writer.

FINDING THE SIMPLER WORD

Reading good writers will put you into the mood to do better yourself. But precisely how do you go about this business of simplifying?

Certainly not by trying to follow the vague precept "Write the way you talk," or the equally impractical "Write the way you would write to your grandmother." Common sense stops us from doing either; it tells us we would sound ridiculous. Our kind of writing must be expository and accurate, even when it is colloquial.

Then how can we do this within limits of the more formal English usually required of us? Obviously, by writing simpler sentences—as I will show later—but first, by selecting our words better, by going over what we have written and throwing out the stiff, the stuffed, the needlessly muscle-bound words.

▶ By weighing every habit-former such as *encounter* and *endeavour*. Do these words, and these words only, convey the thought? If not, switch to the "four-letter" substitutes—*meet* and *try*.

▶ By rejecting every intrusion of bureaucratic and "business" English. It is not enough to shun only nuisance phrases—to change every "It is requested" to "Will you?" Also throw out the nuisance words—change every *finalized* to *finished* or *signed* or *agreed upon*, or some other simpler, more precise expression.

▶ By remembering Fowler's "The better the writer, the shorter his words" when you meet a long, technical word that has no synonym. Why cling to *magnetohydrodynamics* after it has evolved, through necessity, into *hydromagnetics* and then into simply *MHD*?

▶ And certainly by shunning every needlessly compounded word. The trouble is not with the name of the smelly gas but with amateurishly writing it *hydrogensulphide* rather than sticking to *hydrogen sulphide* or H_2S. The trouble is even worse with hyphened horrors. When the hyphen serves a purpose, it needs no apology. Spinoza was a "God-intoxicated man." This is effective, so notable that I remember it where I would quickly have forgotten "a man intoxicated with God." But a little of this goes far enough.

Such *Time* magazine concoctions as "moon-placid temperament," modelled after hyphenations in Homer's *Iliad*, cannot be our standard any more than can the agglutinations found in Homer himself. We can understand that Minerva was a "bright-eyed goddess" but too much of her "dread-tasselled aegis" soon discourages us. And that is simple compared with the double- and triple-jointed words that engineers are asked to read. "The accelerator-pedal-position recorder is connected to . . ." will sing better and ski better when changed to "The accelerator pedal works a position recorder that is connected to . . ." And why "Prescription-filling needs care" when "Filling prescriptions needs care" is so much simpler? The same words are used here but are rearranged for easier understanding.

It is the habit-forming, show-off words that plague our prose most, because they intrude whether we are writing technically or not. Here are two examples:

1. So **versus** *Therefore.* It is understandable that the technician will be interested in cause and effect. But why should the link in his chain of reasoning so constantly be *therefore*—or, for that matter, *consequently, hence, ergo, thus, accordingly*? The little word *so*—only half as long as a four-letter word—is usually just as serviceable, and less pontifical.

True, it can be worked to death. The fact that an architect builds four *ergos* into one pargraph does not justify a train of *so*'s that remind you of a girl relating events of the night before: "So I told him . . . so he answered . . . so we went . . ." and so on. Common sense and literacy cannot be ignored. Moreover, there are several *so*'s. The word can mean *consequently, in that degree, in like manner*. Even two of them in the same sentence can produce a grammatically correct but hardly literate "It was so designed that it worked well, so the contract was awarded."

It is the second *so*, in the sense of *consequently*, that will lift many burdens off your prose. Put it to work. Save the *therefores*, etc., for times when only they can do the job.

2. ***Now* versus *Presently*.** For some reason, *presently* is considered a stylish replacement for *now*. Functionally, in this sense, it offers only one service, that of safety if you are afraid that the typist or printer will strike a wrong key and that the little word *now* will emerge as the little word *not*. If such a typographical error occurred, and it slipped past the proofreader, and you yourself didn't read proof carefully enough, "The heart will now stop" could become "The heart will not stop."

But this is reaching into the bleachers to justify *presently*. It is not only a show-off word, six letters longer than *now*. It is also badly misused. It simply is not a precise synonym for *now*. It does not mean *now*, *the present moment*, *at the moment*. It means *in a moment*, *very soon*. And it should be saved for just such work. Otherwise, how is the poor reader to know which it is you mean if you invariably write *presently*?

These Are Simpler

The two words, *so* and *now*, show the common-sense advantages of simplifying. The first is shorter than *therefore*—no tiresome frills. The second is not only shorter than *presently* but gives a crisper meaning.

The same advantages will be found in the list of simpler words at the end of this chapter. It offers substitutes for words that are affectations, or are not precise enough, or are worked to death—and are often a combination of all three. Most of the words for which substitutes are offered are "long" words, but there are some short ones too. These are the words that end up being long because the writer tries to perk them up with adjectives—an invitation to tautology: *basic* becomes *underlying basis*, *factor* becomes *contributing factor*.

It is easier to edit our writing than our speech. Whenever you write, look for the nuisance words and quickly run a line through them when they cannot justify themselves. Most can be replaced by something better. Some in the list, however, are followed by my (kill?) query because they probably need no replacement. For example, "*achieved* a result" becomes simply "resulted in."

The list should be consulted realistically. A "long" word is not always taboo. It can sometimes serve as a synonym that avoids tiresome repetition. Or it may occur as another part of speech (*implement* is wordy as a verb but useful as a noun); such words are indicated by an asterisk. So is the word that has another and satisfactory meaning (*presently* in the sense of *very soon*).

Most of the listed words oppress nontechnical as well as technical writing. Not included are the nuisances that a technician writes seldom, if ever, such as *gainsay*, when *deny* would do.

If some of the substitutes are not precise enough for a specific need, some of the wordy words are just as faulty. The answer then is to think over your facts better and find a word to suit. But if the choice must be between vague *good* and vague *attractive*, choose the former. The substitute, whether a shorter word or an easy phrase, is often more honest. Always, it is simpler.

Check-list of Simpler Words

(asterisk indicates the word may be needed for a specific meaning)

"Big" Word	Substitute	"Big" Word	Substitute
accelerate*	speed up, go faster	ameliorate	reduce, improve
		antithesis	opposite
accomodate	fit, take	apparent	clear, plain
accomplish	do, carry out	apparently	seems
accordingly	so	applicable	applies, fits
achieve	get, reach (or kill?)	application*	use
		appropriate*	proper
actuate*	start, move	approximately	about
additional	extra, more	ascertain	learn, find out
admissible	allowed	assimilate	absorb, digest
advantageous	useful, good	attempt	try
advise*	tell	attractive	good
aggregate	total, sum	basic	main (or kill?)
agitate	stir, excite	bilateral	two-sided, two-way
alleviate	ease		
ambient*	surrounding	capable	able

Check-list of Simpler Words *(continued)*

characteristic	(as noun, kill?)	*elevated*	high
circuitous	roundabout	*elevation*	height
*coagulate**	thicken	*emphasize*	stress
cognizant	aware	*employ*	use (or kill?)
commence	begin, start	*encounter*	meet
component	part	*endeavour*	try
*conception**	idea, thought	*entirety*	whole
*conclusion**	end	*equivalent*	equal
conference	meeting	*essentially*	(kill?)
*configuration**	pattern	*evaluate*	test, try out
conjecture	guess	*evident*	plain, clear
consequently	so	*evolution*	change, growth
considerable	much	*expedient**	good
consists	has	*expedite*	speed, ease
construct	build, make	*expendable*	useless, worn
contiguous	next to, near, touching	*expenditure*	cost
		experiment	test
continuous	steady, unbroken	*external*	outer
convenient	handy	*fabricate*	make, build
*convey**	give	*facilitate*	ease
criterion	test, rule, standard	*facility*	(kill?)
		*factor**	cause, influence (or kill?)
*decelerate**	slow down		
deficiency	lack	*finalize*	finish, sign, make, agree on
desirable	wanted		
development	growth, change	*formulate*	draw up
diminish	drop, lessen	*fortunately*	(kill?)
diminution	less, decrease, drop	*fragment*	piece
		frequently	often
discussion	talk	*function*	job, task, role
disengage	free, let go	*fundamentally*	(kill?)
disseminate	spread, scatter	*furthermore*	then, also, too
distribute	spread, allot	*generate*	produce, give
*dominant**	main, major, leading	*gravitate*	approach, settle
		hence	so
duplicate	copy	*identical*	same
dynamic	active, swift	*illustrate*	show
effect	make, do, bring about	*immediately*	at once
		impair	harm
effective	works	*imparts*	gives

Check-list of Simpler Words (*continued*)

*implement**	fulfil, complete	*paramount*	main, chief
inapplicable	unsuited	*partially*	partly
inasmuch	because	*penetrate*	pierce, enter
incombustible	fireproof	*periphery*	outer edge
indeterminate	vague	*pertaining*	related
indicate	show	*pictured*	shown
indication	sign	*predominant*	main
ineffectual	useless	*presently**	now
inexpensive	cheap	*principal*	main, chief
inflammable	burns	*prior*	before
initiate	begin, start	*procedure*	way, method
intangible	vague	*proportion*	part
inundate	flood	*prototype**	model
isolate	separate	*provide*	give, allow
jeopardize	risk	*proximity*	near (or kill?)
justification	excuse	*quadrilateral*	four-sided
juxtaposition	alongside, next to	*recognize*	know, accept
		reconstruct	remake
liberate	free	*refrigerate*	cool, freeze
likewise	and, also	*relatively*	(kill?)
luminous	bright, shining	*remainder*	the rest
magnitude	size, range	*reproduction*	copy
*manifest**	plain, clear	*require*	need
manufacture	make	*requisite*	needed
meticulous	exact, neat	*requisition*	demand, call for
mitigate	ease, relieve, lessen	*saturate*	soak, fill
		segment	part
modification	change	*segregate*	separate, sift
necessary	needed	*selection*	choice
necessitate	need, require	*similar*	like
nevertheless	but, however	*situated*	placed, is
objective	aim, goal	*solitary*	lone
oblique	slanting	*stated*	said
observe	see, note	*stringent*	tight, strict
occupy	fill, take up	*subordinate**	lower
operate	work, run	*subsequently*	after, later, then
operational	working	*substantial*	much, large
optimum	best	*sufficient*	enough
orifice	hole	*supersede*	replace
outstanding	main	*symptomatic*	shows

Check-list of Simpler Words *(continued)*

tabulation	list, table	*uniform*	same
technicality	detail	*unique*	(kill?)
technique	way, method	*utilize*	use (or kill?)
terminate	end	*variation*	change
therefore	so	*velocity*	speed
thus	so	*virtually*	almost
transverse	crosswise	*visualize*	see
typical	(kill?)	*vitally*	(kill?)
ultimate	last, final	*voluminous*	bulky, big
unavailability	lack	*withstand*	stand, resist
undulations	waves, curves		

7

WORDS THAT SAY IT BEST

WITH all respect to the simple word and the wonders it can work, it is only a part-time magician. What we need all of the time is the right word, be it short or long, etymologically pure or a bastard.

Too often, whether we are technicians or popularizers, we hear ourselves echoing the cry of tongue-tied Moses in the Schoenberg opera, "Oh word, thou word that I lack!"

Before going on to assemble sentences, then, let's take a last, hard look at the word—the building block of all sentence structure.

I will start by being a bit brutal, by putting words in Charles Darwin's mouth. I will attribute his monumental finding—why man isn't an ape—to "science-love, reflectiveness and collectionizing."

Cryptic? Awkward? Empty? Yes, all of these. The style is ponderous; the reader is forced to ponder. Yet this paraphrasing of what Darwin really said obeys familiar injunctions to write it tight so that the reader can get through it fast. Specifically, I shunned adjectives and other qualifiers. Quick prescriptions for good writing consider such words detestable. I followed those prescriptions.

It should be obvious that too many adjectives can be as bad

as the "and, and, and..." of baby prattle. Too many qualifiers make us suspect a scientist is cagey because his facts are suspect. No adjective can pull a weak or inaccurate noun out of trouble; no adverb can rescue a drowning verb.

But why ban so blindly? Why dismiss the hard workers along with the loafers? In that paraphrasing of Darwin, only the word *and* is easy. The rest is overcompressed. It is shorthand that cries for qualifiers. It's in the tempo that Professor Williard Thorp of Princeton calls "hot-rodding." It's fast writing—so fast that it slows the reader to a standstill.

Darwin didn't write that way. In mythology, Jove's headache gave birth to Minerva, goddess of wisdom. In the nineteenth century, Darwin's chronic migraine gave birth to the theory of evolution. Headaches didn't prevent his brain from functioning nicely. And good thinking feeds capable writing. Here is the way Darwin wrote that explanation. He attributed his success to "the love of science, unbounded patience in reflecting over any subject, industry in observing and collecting facts, and a fair share of invention as well as of common sense."

That makes sense. Darwin hasn't wasted words, nor has he ruptured himself trying to lift overcompressed big ones.

In the same field—the study of man's origin—Julian Huxley describes the duck-billed platypus as "a museum of reptilian reminiscence." Fine. Try writing gifted prose if you are gifted that way. Even then, practice moderation. Even ringing, singing words should not be overabundant or empty; we are not competing with the Elizabethans, or with science-fiction writers. Some of the latter are superb; others simply sizzle with extravagance:

> His knuckles went white with strain and tiny droplets of blood began to form under his fingernails. The humid air choked his throat and a cold sweat beaded his forehead. The massed black clouds rolled over his head like a dark sea suspended in the air. Drums of thunder throbbed in the west and an electric hush charged the atmosphere. Lightning flickered in ghost-flames. It was the Time of the Terror. . . .

As with simple words (preceding chapter), let us seek guidance now to the right words. This may seem surprising—but let's start with the United States Patent Office. It has acquired the reputation of being dull, a "square." But I have read and rewritten patents often, and found most of them palatable. This is because the patent examiners tolerate no nonsense. Here is their prescription:

> Clear disclosure both in specifications and drawings is basic. . . . In exchange for a patent monopoly the inventor must clearly explain his invention. . . . The public is entitled to know the precise limits. . . . A common cause for rejection is that of indefiniteness, where the claims include alternative or negative expressions, terms with no antecedent, indirect limitation of preceding terms, inferential rather than positive recitation of elements, and the like. . . .

That could well be the platform for this chapter on right words. And if the presence of law in the background frightens you, remember that law isn't the only profession that reeks of jargon; that Waldemar Kaempffert, who led the way in science journalism, started as a lawyer; that such lawyers as Thomas Jefferson and Abraham Lincoln were inventors as well as masters of the right word, and that they wrote the Declaration of Independence and Gettysburg Address, respectively.

ADJECTIVES ARE BAD. TRUE OR FALSE?

We hear much about spurning adjectives; adverbs too. We are ordered to write with nouns and verbs: "Good nouns and verbs need no modifiers. Adjectives and adverbs usually weaken and complicate the meaning."

That is a rule found in some books on writing, especially on technical writing, that borrow from each other without critical examination. Did you notice the mountainous qualifiers: "*Good* nouns and verbs"; "adjectives and adverbs *usually* weaken"? Such a rule becomes mere quibbling.

Furthermore, the following would satisfy the rule:

A shower in spring, where an umbrella
And a raincoat walk conversing.

That is a Japanese hokku (also called *haiku*)—deft poetry made up of unqualified nouns and verbs, but a useless model for us.

Gertrude Stein preached the no-adjectives rule, but in her own independent fashion. She preached against nouns too, and she extolled adverbs. Why was she against adjectives? Because they, as well as nouns, are "uninteresting." But verbs and adverbs are interesting. Why?

> In the first place they have one very nice quality and that is that they can be so mistaken. It is wonderful the number of mistakes a verb can make and that is equally true of its adverb. Nouns and adjectives can never make mistakes can never be mistaken but verbs can be so endlessly.

Elsewhere she explains it all: "Complications make eventually for simplicity."

Let us overlook the *nice* and *wonderful* in the quoted passage. Parodying the travelogue writers, let us now say good-by to the swamps cherished by Miss Stein and other obscurantists.

The only sensible answer to the charge against adjectives is that it is half true, half false.

The writer so ensnared by a cliché that his comparative for "well known" becomes "less well known" is treating neither cliché nor modifier kindly. Nor is the radio announcer who describes a programme "that will make your day a little bit more brighter."

But listen to Frank Norris, who, though he deprecated purple passages written by others, also knew that the right adjectives need no apology:

> The plowing, now in full swing, enveloped him in a vague, slow-moving whirl. . . . Underneath him was the jarring, jolting, trembling machine . . . the very friction of the damp soil, sliding incessantly from the shiny surface of the shears, seemed to reproduce itself in his finger-tips and along the back of his head . . . and all along the line the voices of the men talking to the horses. Everywhere there were visions of glossy brown backs, straining, heaving, swollen with muscle; harness streaked with specks of froth; broad cup-shaped hoofs, heavy with brown loam; men's faces red with tan, blue overalls spotted with axle-grease . . . and more penetrating than anything else, the heavy enervating odor of the upturned, living earth.

Norris' adjectives are not abstract, overworked, lazy. They are the precise kind that appeal to our senses of touch, sight, smell. When, then, do adjectives turn bad?

▶ When they are too wordy, smell of jargon, have the "Learned Look." These are the adjectives you strain for. They remind me of the letter received by Wilfred Funk's department on word-power in *Reader's Digest*:

> I wish you would give me the names as many as you can that applies to a person that is, insolent, contemptious, callous, contumacious. I have to use these words often and if there is any others I wish you would enumerate them for me.

▶ When they are too cute. Thus, the weary sophisticate who dismissed botany and zoology with:

> The country is a damp sort of place where all sorts of birds fly about uncooked.

▶ When they are downright inaccurate. One music critic says "Appalachian Spring" is "dry and somewhat stern"; another describes it as "fragile and lovely." Very well, this is just the subjectiveness of art jargon. Different newspapermen attending a White House press conference describe the same President Eisenhower as "ruddy" and as "pale." Very well, they weren't equipped with spectrometer and colorimeter. Technicians cannot justify themselves so easily. Army engineers who prepared specifications for the St. Lawrence Seaway labelled the subsoil as "compact to very compact." Contractors thought this would let them carve their way with power shovels. Instead, they had to dynamite. Contending that the adjective should have been "cemented," they demanded an extra $7 million.

▶ When they are ambiguous. We have already met compound adjectives that lack a needed hyphen, such as in "severely competitive billion dollar vegetable oil refining industry" and "a steam coils containing vat." We have also seen the dangers in two-faced adjectives—such as "flexible machinery," instead of "versatile machinery." In addition, technicians are too fond of fudge-words like *small, great, fortunately.* Would you trust data from the researcher who writes, "This information will give rather accurate measurements"? If he cannot be precise, why not "sufficiently accurate measurements"? Hazy adjectives cannot help us decide whether a French cartridge will fit a British rifle, whether a gyro wheel for space travel is correctly positioned to within tolerances of millionths of an inch. Even *exquisite* is a better workman than *small* and *fortunate*. Just as technology brought in *sophisticated* to describe highly complex but admirable apparatus, the Supreme Court neatly scorned the Agriculture Department's Milk Marketing Orders for being "exquisitely complicated."

NOUNS ARE GOOD. TRUE OR FALSE?

Though Miss Stein detested them, nouns are eulogized by the usual run of adjective-hating verb-lovers. Like the girl with the curl on her forehead, when nouns are good, they are very, very good; and when they are bad, they are horrid. Let us concede their worthiness, especially when they name concrete things, and go on to see where the dangers lie.

▶ The simplest problem, but a chronic one, is that of spelling. Nouns are born in all sorts of places and don't follow the spelling rules as carefully as do other parts of speech. Writing "resourcinol" for "resorcinol" is merely an error. But why "computer" and not "computor"; why, on the other hand, "calculator" and not "calculater"? I call the problem simple because there is always the dictionary. If it cannot tell us the difference between egoist and egotist, why waste time arguing? One is as correct as the other.

▶ More serious, often more so than with other parts of speech, is the wrong choice of word. A solvent is not a solute, nor is a neuron a neutron. Straining for an unusual noun may produce nothing worse than a malapropism or a *"clutch* of kangaroos." But there can be explosive results when you confuse percussion cap with fuse, or nitrite with nitrate. Throughout our kind of writing, there must always be sharp fences between words—the realization that we just don't have as many synonyms as we would like, that *size* and *dimension*, *density* and *specific gravity*, are almost as far apart as are *quality* and *quantity*.

▶ Nouns naming abstract things can be as weak as any adjective, adverb—or verb, too—that lacks force. *Truth* is less serviceable to us than *facts*. And even facts need care: *data*, *hypotheses*, *conjectures*, *proposals* should be stood up where they can be seen. Add weak adjective to weak noun and you produce something "of a weak nature."

▶ The noun is too often retained—in a weak noun-phrase—when it should be transformed into a shorter and stronger verb form. "For the manufacture of" reads more easily and says more when it becomes "to make" or "for manufacturing." The fault here is the same infatuation with nouns that produces such hash as *finalization*, *ideation* and *definitization*.

▶ The biggest trouble with nouns is their fondness for dwelling in the jargon jungle. This is the land of "desuperheaters" and "tensegrity" that we have already explored, in Chapter 5.

▶ Close cousin to the jargon noun is the one that confuses by not telling enough. Calling something *machine* is insufficient. Calling it *instrument* is no more helpful than the adjective *instrumental* or the verb *instrumented*. Such nouns might as well be *dingus* or *gismo* for all the help they give the reader. Be specific—call it a *grinder*, *oscilloscope*, *indexer*, *probe*, or whatever else it really is.

ADVERBS ARE GOOD. TRUE OR FALSE?

Their faults are many. They have solid virtues too. It is nonsense to say it doesn't matter whether "a reaction goes" or "a reaction goes swiftly." What does matter is not explaining that the reaction is finished in a second.

▶ In general, badly chosen adverbs share the faults of badly chosen adjectives. Some are much too eager. Convert the noisy adjectives *wild* and *furious* into adverbs by adding *ly* and you have brakes that "shriek wildly" and liquids that "boil furiously."

▶ Like adjectives, adverbs are often too vague or ambiguous. Lazy adverbs like *much*, *low*, *well* don't say enough. "Very weakened condition" doesn't tell how weak. "Very much corroded" is cause for alarm—but how dangerously corroded? The adjective *fortunate* has its overbusy adverb *fortunately*, and *unfortunately* is the technician's best-loved alibi word. Behind it stand such other loophole adverbs as *unduly*, *comparatively*, *relatively*.

The operation is relatively safe, the scientists said. It has been tried on about 30 dogs. Five of them are alive and well.

▶ But some adverbs are as precise as you can wish. "It was deservedly popular" tells much more than "It was popular." A suitable adverb is not only shorter than a lazy noun-phrase but more exact. Thus: "The facts and the interpretation were announced at the same time." Same time as what? A precise adverb steps in: "The facts and the interpretation were announced simultaneously." Furthermore, as we will see at the end of this chapter, it's in the adverb family that we find most of those effective savers of space and sharpeners of meaning, the "influence" words.

▶ Everybody who has written an awkward sentence knows that a big problem with adverbs is where to place them. But every experienced writer knows that this syntax problem evaporates when you consult, not the rules, but the common sense upon which rules are built. Obviously, the adverb should modify what it is intended to. But it is less obvious to beginners that the adverb should be placed where it sounds most natural—usually positioned as close as possible to the word or word group it modifies. This problem will be examined further in Chapter 9 (page 137).

VERBS ARE GOOD. TRUE OR FALSE?

Again the criteria for our kind of writing are precision, accuracy, effectiveness, space-saving. When the verb is active, when it really does things, it is a splendid helper. It destroys, creates, speeds, paralyzes, boosts, overcomes, freezes, boils, surpasses, matches, drops, rises. It shatters, strengthens, weakens. It outworks, outweighs, outperforms, outdistances. But when it merely compares, it might as well be dead.

> *Bad:* Sample A weighs 35 grams compared with 70 grams for Sample B.

> *Good:* Sample A weighs 35 grams, half as much as Sample B.

> *Good:* Sample B outweighs Sample A by 35 grams.

Here are the troubles that lurk in verbs:
▶ The technician surrenders too easily to overworked words like *involvement*. His method of calculating price curves may be *involved* (complicated). But he is not *involved* in every meeting,

every calculation, every decision. He *attends* meetings, *calculates* prices, *participates* in decisions.

▶ Verbs can be the laziest of all parts of speech—the worst sayers of nothing when they join other words in devouring valuable space. "It appears that . . ."; "It should be noted that . . ."; "It is essential that . . ." Sometimes these are helpful. Most often they are padding that should be ripped out of the language of science—and out of all writing.

▶ Even when verbs do say something, it is frequently not enough. *Compare* is one example. Here are three other verbs that every expositional writer should regard with a brutally critical eye.

Use. Because *use*, both as verb and noun, is such a pest, many word-shops try banning it. I did this once, and paid for my arbitrariness. My writers simply turned to other lazy words. Instead of *using*, they *employed*, they *utilized*, they *availed themselves of*. These overworked substitutes didn't help me or the reader; they were just as vague and took more space.

The correct substitute, of course, is the right word. Instead of a transistor being *used as*, maybe it can *serve as*; instead of a thermometer being *used with*, maybe it can be *included with* or *incorporated in*. The more specific, the better. The scale isn't *used* to get the weight; it *weighs*. He doesn't *use* a second washer; he *adds* a second washer. The brake isn't *used* as an automatic control; it automatically *stops* something. The carpenter doesn't *use* a saw to cut; he *cuts* with a saw, or *saws*.

Why "It *uses* a fuse" when there are so many substitutes that tell more? It *includes* a fuse, or *relies on* a fuse, or *gets safety* from a fuse, or *is made safe* with a fuse; a fuse *is added*, or its fuse *is* 15 amps, or, even, it *has* a fuse. Each variation sharpens the meaning in its own way and there is no danger unless you try becoming dynamic and say, "It is fused."

In short, instead of my saying "*Use* is a verb not to use," I can deliver my warning less negatively and more realistically: "*Use* is a verb to avoid whenever you can."

Be. This is the most necessary verb in the language. But its mistakes and laziness have blackened its reputation.

In one form or another, it constantly gets the writer into

grammar trouble. For example, "Two times two is four" and "Two times two are four" are equally correct. But "What is needed is four motors" is correct and "What is needed are four motors" is incorrect. The practical writer doesn't let this harass him. If the choice is perplexing, he dodges it—with another verb, or by recasting.

Another verb: Two times two equals four.

Recasting: Four motors are needed.

The other problem with *be* stems from its innate weakness as a verb. Only rarely, as in the whisky ad that was changed from "Clear heads agree Calvert *tastes* better" to ". . . . *is* better," does it give a more positive connotation. Usually its passivity, whether it's alone or auxiliary to a participle, makes it the weaker choice:

Weak: The patient was operated upon by us.

Strong: We operated on the patient.

Describe. The cure here is to find appropriate synonyms. For example, if you are reviewing industrial literature for your company or a magazine, why should every incoming folder, booklet, brochure and catalogue be one that "*describes*"? Escape deadly repetition and give the reader more enlightenment. That literature may also *contain, provide, list, outline, explain, cover, show, define, discuss, illustrate.*

CLICHES ARE BAD. TRUE OR FALSE?

It is appropriate that the French, who gave us such worshippers of the right word as Gide and Flaubert, should also have supplied "cliché" as label for the trite word or phrase. But, as I reminded you when we examined jargon, we happen to live in a real world.

We cannot hang up a sign saying "No Clichés Allowed Here." Some were born honourably, some are slang. All have become established and we all use them, whether we are writing good science in bad English or bad science in good English. We would become dumb if we paused to examine every word for its triteness content. Today's new word becomes tomorrow's cliché. The editor who objected to nearly everything as "corny" was himself being corny.

As with jargon, the best we can do here is sin as seldom as possible. Some clichés are easily detectable becuase they are so deathly tired—"history tells us," "mine of information," "food for thought." Others reach heights of ridiculousness, as in this metaphor-mixing: "I regret to inform you that the hand that rocked the cradle has kicked the bucket." Still others heap tautology upon cliché—"full details will be spelled out."

Only precision, or lack of it, can guide our choice. *Fabulous* was never for science writing, and less so when it became a cliché. "Little-know facts" and "well-known findings" are among the favourite dodges of the writer who isn't sure of his facts and findings, and of the advertiser who doesn't care to state them. At the very least, we can shun the illiteracy of "The most well-known serum was discussed at the University of . . ."

REPETITION IS BAD. TRUE OR FALSE?

If the machine is a grinder, be specific and call it grinder. But choosing the right word doesn't justify falling so in love with it that you can't let it go, as in "the most versatile grinder in this shop is a grinder that grinds . . ."

Here are less obvious ways of wearying the reader with repetition:

Wrong: The thermometer indicates the point at which the temperature of the liquid becomes explosive. (*Following* thermometer, *the words* point *and* temperature *become synonymous, so take your pick.*)

Right: The thermometer indicates the explosion point of the liquid (*or,* . . . the explosion temperature of the liquid).

Wrong: This will be the best antibiotic for many future years to come. (*Here we have the sneaky kind of redundancy called tautology.* Future = years to come; *choose one or the other; you can't have both.*)

Wrong: It felt warm to the touch. (*More tautology.*)

Wrong: The experiment was again given another try. (*Tautology.*)

But there are dangers in too blindly avoiding repetition. The cub reporter is straining mighty hard when he calls the creature an elephant in one sentence and pachyderm (rather than just *it*) in the second; and the strain leads to error when he calls another creature a whale in the first sentence and a giant fish in the second. The technician, too, often forgets the main reason for consulting dictionary and thesaurus. Synonyms in these books are seldom exact duplicates. Their value is in allowing choice of the precise shade of meaning needed. If no synonym will do, stick to the original word, or recast the sentence.

Repetition is also best when recasting will merely introduce trouble with antecedents. In the following you may not be elegant but you are safe against introducing an ambiguous *it*:

> No ordinary container for such a gas could be devised. To hold the gas, the container would have to . . .

Repetition can even add punch if handled skilfully:

> For Brutus is an honourable man;
> So are they all, all honourable men.

> The common cold is the most annoying and humiliating illness with which your doctor has to deal. His annoyance and humiliation are increased if he has to interrupt his recommendations to you while he clears his own nose or throat.

These are exceptions. It is usually best to dodge repetition—and do it purposefully rather than defensively.

Example 1. Suppose I mention "gears" three times in the same paragraph. Each reference is clear enough, but the second two are wasteful. Now suppose I write: "The gears are made of special steel . . . these components fit into a case . . . the gear train has a higher speed-reduction ratio . . ." I have not merely been avoiding the same word; I have been choosing the right ones. I started simply, with "gears," and named the material; next, with "components," I stress that they are part of an assembly; next, with "gear train," I indicate that they work together.

Example 2. Suppose I mention "nylon" four times in the same paragraph. Again, that's safe. But suppose I write: "The bearing is made of nylon . . . the material is strong and light . . . this pioneer among plastics . . . a characteristic of this polyamide . . ." Each synonymous reference has advanced the exposition: what we're doing with the nylon, how it rates among materials, where it stands among plastics—and I even give its chemical-family name.

INFLUENCE WORDS? THEY'RE GOOD

Right at the tip of your tongue are some of the most effective words in the language. It's only your fault if you don't work them. Though small words, they are powerful: they cue and sharpen the sentence and paragraph. All good craftsmen keep them busy.

Let's call them the "influence words." It doesn't matter what parts of speech they are, though most are adverbs. Let's examine one, *only*.

Lazy wording would say a refrigerator design is "optimal." The more precise writer prefers something better. He writes: "The refrigerator cools rapidly, defrosts easily, and costs little."

Now bring in *only*; the sentence becomes persuasive indeed: "The refrigerator *not only* cools rapidly; it defrosts easily and costs little." Or, for emphasis elsewhere, he inserts a second influence word, *yet*: "The refrigerator costs *only* $100, *yet* it cools rapidly and defrosts easily."

There we had *only* as an adverb. It is equally influential as an adjective. For example: "Its speed was 60 m.p.h. compared with lesser speeds for the others." Now insert *only*: "It was the *only* vehicle that reached 60 m.p.h."

Verbs, of course, can be influential too—in the foregoing revision I also strengthened *was* with the active verb *reached*. The number of influential verbs is limited only by the span of your vocabulary: by the number of active verbs you can substitute for passive ones, sharp verbs for dull ones.

"The temperature was 500 degrees Centigrade" gains power—and precision—when changed to "The temperature soared to 500 degrees Centigrade." "This motor is 50 pounds heavier than the other" is inferior to "This motor outweighs the other by 50 pounds."

Even relatively weak verbs can be given a blood transfusion. This is no more complicated than inserting *only* at the right place. Pair the rather lazy verb *did* with another influence word, the conjunction *though*, and you get: "*Though* it was an estimate, it *did* show the possibilities."

The problem arises: How far are you allowed to sharpen otherwise dull facts? How much interpretation per how much fact? And how precise can a word be anyway?

We need not bog down in semantics to realize that "loaded" words can be dangerous. A reputable newspaper is chary of "bloated capitalist" and "conniving Communist," of "snaggle-toothed" and "beady-eyed." It carefully weighs the differences among "claimed," "asserted," "said to," "alleged," "accused of," "described as."

Such are the hazards in any writing that must withstand pressures from interested parties. Words are not only slanted deliberately; they are even turned topsy-turvy, and quite innocently. *Nearsighted* really means that you see well at short distances, badly at long distances. *Farsighted* is the reverse. But a truly farsighted person tells the doctor he is nearsighted—that is, he cannot read comfortably. No matter. He knows what he means, and so does the doctor who prescribes the glasses for farsightedness.

In all this, the technician need only follow common usage. Neither he nor anybody else can insist on semantic perfection. But in his own field he must be more cautious, especially with short words that carry much power. He should never say *never*, at least hardly ever. Like *all-time* it claims too much. So do *all*, *no*, *always*—these are truly big words. Handle with care.

An influence word like *only* could also be dangerous, if brought in as a sneer: "She is only a lab. assistant"; "He is only a foreigner." But the sneering technician would be writing propaganda, not science. Handled honestly, influence words do not impair scientific objectivity. They do damage the pompous, excessive worship of objectivity, the overcautiousness that prefers vagueness to frankness. It is not propagandistic to change "20 times as strong as present materials" to "20 times stronger than present materials"; or to sum up by saying ". . . And that is why the process is superior."

It is not objectivity but overlooking your duty to write merely, "The pressure reaches 300 p.s.i. in this tank designed to take 275 p.s.i." The possibility of trouble should be stressed: "The pressure in this tank reaches 300 p.s.i.—25 p.s.i. beyond the safety point." Here the influence word *beyond* was teamed with the specific words *safety point*. Result: a clear and present danger.

Influence words operate in several ways. In the foregoing example, *beyond* served as an alarm. It was more specific, less amateurish, than the promiscuous underlining of words you want to stress, or closing the sentence with an exclamation point. Usually, however, such words are not intended to be dramatic. Their job is to help the reader—help him follow the thought, connect evidence with conclusion and cause with effect. The reader is shown the relationship, is helped to appraise, is given the facts in better perspective.

In the example of good writing by the Atomic Energy Commission (Chapter 1, page 11), you saw such influential words as *only* and *simply* at work clarifying the discussion of deuterium. In the following passage, Professor H. D. Smyth of Princeton is describing the epochal research that gave us atomic power. Remember that his official report, *Atomic Energy for Military Purposes*, was not so-called "popular science." It was written for scientists and engineers. But Smyth continually called in influential words (shown here in italic) to point out the path:

> In the first stages *even* the routine analysis of samples had to be done by remote control . . . *but* the combination of its alpha-ray activity and chemical properties makes it one of the most dangerous substances known. . . . *However*, the *really* troublesome materials are the fission products . . . *of course*, possible pollution of the adjacent river must be considered. *In fact*, the standards of safety set were *so* strict that . . . *Eventually*, the process is stopped *long before* this stage is reached.

That book was for specialists. The following passage from *The Great Decision*, by a more popular writer, Michael Amrine, also chronicles the early days of the atomic bomb. At their meeting in Potsdam, President Truman told the Soviet dictator that America had a powerful new bomb—now note how much Amrine adds with the simple words *but* and *neither*:

Stalin seemed strangely unimpressed. But Truman had not used the word "atomic." Neither had he used the word "nuclear."

Any word that has power is persuasive. The very active verbs, for instance. Or the many adverbs—usually formed from adjectives—that cue the reader: *deceptively, dangerously, surprisingly,* and the like.

Listed below are some examples of simpler influence words at work. In themselves they are not dramatic at all. It is hard to believe that they can be persuasive. But plant them, even in short sentences, and they quickly turn dullness into sharpness.

actually
> It seemed a failure. We learned this from it . . .
> It seemed a failure; actually, it taught us this . . .

also
> His pulse was low and his blood count was subnormal.
> His pulse was low. His blood count was also subnormal.

although
> The motor had good power with low voltage.
> Although voltage was low, the motor had sufficient power.

and
> It was erected carefully, then it collapsed.
> It was erected carefully—and it collapsed.

barely
> Plane production was a few units short of the quota.
> Plane production barely missed reaching the quota.

because
> There was drought and the crop failed.
> The crop failed because of drought.

besides
> It was a weak structure that cost too much.
> Besides costing too much, it was a weak structure.

both
> Each of the two rockets has the same thrust.
> Both rockets have equal thrust.

but
> This is not the answer. There is another.
> This is not the answer, but there is one.

even

The plane exceeded the speed of sound.
The plane flew even faster than the speed of sound.

finally

We reached this conclusion after many tests.
Finally, after many tests, we reached this conclusion.

hardly

The new fruit is small and cannot be expected to . . .
The new fruit is so small it can hardly be expected to . . .

however

The prompt reply we received was obscure.
The reply was prompt; however, it was obscure.

neither

The two high-fidelity systems did not give us good music.
Neither high-fidelity system gave us good music.

only

The first tests were successful. It failed in the last one.
It failed only in the last test.

so

The orbit was predicted well and deviation was no longer a problem.
The orbit was predicted so well that deviation was no longer a problem.

such

Two pieces of the metal can be joined by welding, brazing, soldering, etc.
Two pieces of the metal can be joined by such methods as welding, brazing and soldering.

that

There can be no other reason for the failure.
That, and that alone, caused the failure.

too

This has its good points as well as the other.
This, too, has it good points.

8

SENTENCES THAT MOVE FASTER

IF a straight line is the shortest distance between two points, it is equally true that a simple sentence is the shortest distance between writer and reader. But what are the road directions for a simple sentence?

What is all this about passive versus positive? About loose versus periodic? And what about positioning? Shall the important words be at the beginning, or serve as a clincher at the end of the sentence?

In short, does simple sentence always mean clear sentence and does clear sentence always mean short sentence? In Wolcott Gibbs' celebrated parody describing the birth of the inverted style that became one of *Time* magazine's characteristics, we read: "Backward ran sentences until reeled the mind."

He could as well have parodied the jargon of those less brash writers, the grammarians. Isn't it just possible that their rules are not as important as the practical needs that gave birth to the rules; that common sense might be a safer guide than rules that conflict or confuse; that the technician has an advantage because, having been exposed to the disciplines of science, he can look upon syntax as he does an equation? The sentence either balances, makes sense—or it doesn't.

With this method he can see at a glance what Polish-born Joseph Conrad couldn't when he bumped into English grammar. In a letter concerning a short story that he was planning, he wrote: "It's to be in a nautical setting, and its subject is (or are?) potatoes."

No need to consult Fowler—just speak that sentence. Saying "The subject are potatoes" sounds as incongruous as saying that one equals two.

So let's examine sentence simplicity in terms of the questions we frequently face, but in a functional sense, as practical rather than theoretical problems of fitting words together. This chapter logically follows the chapters on words. They showed that the simpler and more precise words are also the seemingly effortless ones. To woo the reader, sentences should seem effortless too. Their building blocks should go together as neatly and compactly as bricks in a wall.

SPLIT AND PRUNE

Nothing that follows hereafter or has been written in any or all of the preceding chapters, or any parts thereof, shall be construed as being critical of the legal profession other than to the extent that the legal profession has, as alleged, a superabundance of the same faults of long-windedness that are found in other communicative professions, including those professions that are concerned exclusively with the craft of writing.

That is a parody, not my usual style. It merely means that lawyers aren't the only ones who drown us in sentences that are suffocating because they are so long-winded.

But let us keep our heads about this. The longer sentence is not necessarily tedious and the shorter sentence is not necessarily clear. Either can be loaded with verbiage, just as either can be so badly condensed that it is cryptic. Short sentences are the prescription given by some pedants and stylists. Those of us who work in "shirt sleeves"—whether we do books or prepare memoranda, write for newspapers or magazines, edit journals or manuals, compose research papers or assemble advertisements—are less likely to be dogmatic. We know that the longer sentence often carries the thought better. We also respect it as an economy device. By combining two or three shorter sentences, we can frequently say the same thing in fewer words.

Preference? Certainly any writer—especially the technician intent on clarity—should prefer shorter sentences. That is as far as decree can go. To show parallelism or a sequence, you must often write sentences whose elements are linked by semicolons in the classic fashion of a logical Francis Bacon: "Reading maketh a full man; conference a ready man; and writing an exact man."

And to save space you must often drop in a semicolon, a colon, or a dash, and keep on going. Even popularization cannot rely entirely on firecracker sentences. This passage from a magazine illustrates the point:

> The engineers begin to relax. The launching is normal. But this relief is short-lived; seconds later a grim-faced technician turns from a telemetering panel:
> "Something's gone wrong. I think the bird blew up."
> Only one thing can tell the story: the little box inside the missile—an instrument that reaches out, snatches seconds from time, expands them into minutes and then hands them back to engineers for study.

Note here the one sense in which the length of sentences does have importance. Stylistically, a competent writer changes pace. He doesn't limit himself to long sentences or to strings of firecrackers. He balances long sentences against short. Even Samuel Johnson, in an age renowned for its massive sentences, knew the value of tossing forth a staccato "No man but a blockhead ever wrote except for money." But this matter of changing pace is more important to effectiveness than to clarity, and will be mentioned again in the last chapter, on style.

Contrasted with long sentences, overlong sentences are abominable. I have already given many examples and shown how to chop them down so that the meaning will be more direct. Here is another. In front of me is a sentence that begins "Although . . ." and runs on for 112 words. This monster can and should be cut into several shorter sentences. It ends: ". . . and as a consequence it may be that sight has been lost of the possibility of this arrangement for use in recording low temperatures." Kill the first word, *and*, and the rest can stand as a sentence.

But that is not the craftsman's solution. Why not this? "The result is that we may have overlooked the possibility of using this arrangement for recording low temperatures." Now the 24 words have been cut to 18, and the sentence has gained clarity too.

This is shortening that is effective. On the other hand, look at Francis Bacon's epigram again. It would not have gained in clarity or effectiveness—and would have gained five more words—if he had "trichotomized" the sentence: "Reading maketh a full man. Conference maketh a ready man. But it is writing that maketh an exact man."

Even a crisp modern writer like Roger Burlingame knows when to expand:

> More than 10 years before this an American, George Selden, had applied for a patent on a buggy to be moved by the successive explosions of gas in a new kind of engine.

That, of course, could be split:

> Something significant had happened 10 years before that. An American, George Selden, had applied for a patent on a buggy. This vehicle was to be moved by the successive explosions of gas in a new kind of engine.

But to what purpose? The three sentences tell no more, are actually less effective, and, to retain the meaning, require five additional words.

What do these examples show? Simply this. Technology is complicated enough without describing it in complicated sentences, whether they be long or short. When the long sentence accomplishes nothing more than to increase complexity of an already complex subject, it should be simplified. Here are two ways.

1. Splitting. This is quickest. It is easiest when clauses have been strung together with commas for no good reason other than possibly laziness—the so-called "comma fault."

> *Lazy:* The electrons occupy orbital positions around the nucleus, this has been likened to the sun and its planets.

Split: The electrons occupy orbital positions around the nucleus. This has been likened to the sun and its planets. (*But a better-written single sentence here is superior:* The electrons occupy orbital positions around the nucleus—something like the sun and its planets.)

Afterthoughts can also be split off with ease. Sometimes they are merely lazy appendages; sometimes they are qualifiers thrown in for alibi purposes. It often pays to recast inferior wording while you split.

Lazy: The best-known flying knife was invented by Dr. J. I. Guillotin prior to the French Revolution, as a punitive device.

Split: The best-known flying knife was invented by Dr. J. I. Guillotin prior to the French Revolution. It was a punitive device that . . .

Alibi: Here is a scientific principle that is valid provided allowance is made for conditions that make it untrue.

Recast: This scientific principle works part of the time. It is invalid when . . .

Recast: This scientific principle works in most cases. Exceptions are . . .

Combined splitting and recasting also cures awkwardness at the beginning of a sentence. Suppose I write, "In the winter I get up . . ." The rest of that sentence doesn't matter; it is off to a clear start. But suppose the introductory portion is long or complicated: "In the winter time when temperatures in the morning have dropped too low for comfort I get out of bed very reluctantly." A comma after *comfort* will help, but the reader will bless you for splitting off the introduction, and recasting. "On winter mornings, temperatures are too low for comfort. That is why I get out of bed very reluctantly."

When you cannot or do not want to set parenthetical expressions between parentheses, flanking them with commas or dashes is an alternative. But this, too, easily degenerates into awkwardness.

Lazy: Corrosion resistance, important because it imparts strength and longer life while improving the appearance of the product, is difficult to obtain.

Split: Corrosion resistance is difficult to obtain. But it is important because it adds to the strength and life of the product, while improving its appearance.

2. Pruning. Long or short, a sentence can be much too wordy. The obvious cure is to remove needless words and phrases. Though this may require recasting the sentence, running a pencil through the verbiage is frequently enough.

This pruning operation can be as uncomplicated as changing "tetrahedral structure" to "tetrahedron." Or, while you prune, you can also improve the sentence as a whole. For example, the little word *of* is constantly and unnecessarily with us. Removing it also makes the thought more positive: "gathering of information" becomes "gathering information"; "restoration of the rheostat" becomes "restoring the rheostat." But why stop with *of*? "Used for fuel purposes" becomes "used for fuel"; "the fact that he had not succeeded" becomes "his failure"; and, of course, "owing to the fact that" becomes "because."

The process is easily carried still further.

Wordy: Efficiency of the combination would not be as great as for the fuel cell alone.

Better: Efficiency of the combination would not match that of the fuel cell alone.

Wordy: This is decided by the arrangement of electrons within the configuration of the crystal.

Better: This is decided by the way electrons are arranged in the crystal.

Wordy: It is a process which corrodes the metals.

Better: This process corrodes the metals.

But beware of this pitfall for the beginner: turning cryptic in the desire to save a word or two. "Material advantages" is badly ambiguous when you mean to say "advantages of the material"; "part manufacture" is another common blunder—better stick to "manufacture of the parts." Leave false economy to the over-speedy publicity announcement that reports, "Two monkeys were acquired to train animal caretakers."

I

ACCENT THE POSITIVE

It is a commonplace that you should prefer the positive sentence to the negative, the active verb to the passive. These injunctions usually come up in theoretical discussions of style. They are just as germane to the functional writing we are discussing here. The positive statement not only has more force; it has more clarity and often needs fewer words. The same is true of the active verb. Both go together. And you have probably noticed how often, when clarifying an example of ambiguity, I have remedied other faults of the sentence too—simply by recasting it to make it more positive.

When you make a sentence more blunt you sharpen its meaning. Let's examine this strategy a little closer.

> If a diaphragm pulsates at high frequency, a coating with particularly good adhesion to the base fabric and high abrasion resistance is chosen.

What's wrong there? (1) It starts off "iffy." (2) It ends with a weak passive, "is chosen." (3) Its meaning is muddy— "to the base fabric" interrupts the thought, and we have to go back searching for the word *coating*.

Now to simplify that needlessly complex sentence. Why the "If"? And, at the end, who is chooser? What we mean is, "A diaphragm pulsating at high frequency needs . . ." Very well, why not say so? In turning positive we get rid of the "If" beginning and simultaneously banish the weak "is chosen" at the other end. The rest is simple—just reshuffle the "adhesion" and "abrasion resistance":

> A diaphragm pulsating at high frequency needs a coating with particularly high abrasion resistance and good adhesion to the base fabric.

Or, to sharpen the meaning still more:

> A diaphragm pulsating at high frequency needs a coating with particularly high abrasion resistance. It must also adhere well to the base fabric.

Another example:

This steel should not be galvanized without first treating it with acid.

The "be galvanized" is passive, but not badly so. The main trouble is the negativity. The writer forces the reader to begin equating: Do the two negatives equal a positive? A sentence like that can be remedied in several ways. The remedy will depend on the exact meaning desired and on contextual relationship with neighbouring sentences. However, let's examine some alternatives:

This steel must first be treated with acid; otherwise, it cannot be galvanized successfully. (*Remains negative, passive, and has become wordy.*)

Before galvanizing this steel, it is necessary to treat it with acid. (*Shorter, and a useful influence word*—before—*but still sounds wordy, and we have trouble now with* it.)

Before it is galvanized, this steel must be treated with acid. (*Terse enough and satisfactory if context allows, but still part passive.*)

This steel requires treatment with acid before it can be galvanized. (*Less terse, still part passive.*)

Treatment with acid is necessary before galvanizing this steel. (*Satisfactory if context allows*—*emphasizes acid treatment.*)

Acid treatment must precede the galvanizing of this steel. (*Answers all objections.*)

Acid treatment must precede galvanizing this steel. (*Usage allows dropping the word* the *ahead of, and the word* of *after, that gerund* galvanizing—*but a bit crytic. Suitable for a tight caption.*)

Before galvanizing this steel, treat it with acid. (*Answers all objections; crisp and clear.*)

This recasting of sentences to simplify them and accentuate the positive leads quickly to another question: Where, in a sentence, should the emphasis be placed? The instructional writer's "Draw a line . . ." is clearly superior to "A line is drawn . . ." but where, normally, should the words be placed on which you want stress to fall? Like the split infinitive, this provides a frequent conversation piece.

Many scholars feel that the most emphatic position is at the end of the sentence, the next best at the beginning. The shirt-sleeves approach is less dogmatic.

Journalism usually prefers punch at the beginning—it wants to inform the reader quickly. Advertising people tailor the sentence to the need. A newspaper delivery van drives by, flaunting its announcement of a series of exposé articles, "Food, Facts, Fads, Phonies." Under other circumstances, it might read, "Phony Facts on Foods and Fads." The commodity called "good literature" shows no rigidity. Some writers string one eruptive sentence after another, some prefer dawdling, others build up to a climax.

When we write functionally, clarity warns it is better not to be over suspensive; to side, instead, with the journalists. When in doubt, begin at the beginning, but let judgment supervise the rule, if it can be called that:

Questions that arise concerning vacuum tubes and transistors cause rivalry between them. (*The important word* rivalry *is bogged down near the end; too wordy.*)

There is a rivalry between vacuum tubes and transistors caused by questions concerning them. (*Weak and wordy even though* rivalry *has moved up front.*)

Rivalry between vacuum tubes and transistors brings up these questions: . . . (*Strong beginning; end is almost as strong, persuading the reader to continue. And, of course, fewer words.*)

Apparently there is something more vital than the question of beginning or end. Undoubtedly, in the following passage from an engineering paper, the last two words desperately need rescuing:

Under prolonged and severe corrosive conditions, where alkali is formed rapidly and in large amounts, undercutting, due to destruction of surface treatment, or complete destruction of the paint film, if the vehicle is alkali sensitive, can occur.

But in the next example, position is of minor importance compared with the need to split the sentence:

The paddles contain solar cells that convert the sunlight into electric energy which charges the nickel-cadmium batteries that make the transmitter run.

And this passage by Norbert Wiener, the cybernetics specialist and writer, would leave most readers gasping:

If we use to achieve our purposes a mechanical agency with whose operation we cannot efficiently interfere once we have started its action, as for example for the reason that its action is so fast and irrevocable that we have not the data to intervene before the action is complete, then we had better be quite sure that the purpose put into the machine is the purpose which we really desire and not merely a colorable imitation of it.

Our first thought might be that the passage needs tighter punctuation—more commas. But now look at another writer's sentence:

The problem of determining a linkage capable of moving a plane system through three given coplanar positions is trivial.

Obviously a weak statement. The reader has anticipated something more worthwhile than triviality. More commas would not help.

Each of the last two examples is what we call a periodic sentence. The thought isn't completed—you don't get the meaning—until the end. Such sentences can be very effective. But the first discourages us long before the end, and the second ends with something hardly worth saying.

The opposite is what we call a loose sentence: It continues after the main statement is complete. But remember that this type can be spoiled by lazy appendages.

In the last chapter I warned against the word *never*. Now, however, I am tempted to use it. You will never go wrong if you remember clarity. Start with the main subject if you wish:

He went on anyway, without a chance of success.

Or start with the subordinate phrase:

Without a chance of success, he went on anyway.

In the latter, do not be misled. "Without a chance of success" is positive indeed, and here, placing it where it would not normally occur, underlines its force. But the main thing is: Both versions are clear.

PHRASES THAT TALK TOO MUCH

When one of Winston Churchill's generals sent him a memo that began with "Having regard to the fact that . . ." it was returned with this scrawl, "You have used six words where one of two letters—namely, 'as'—would have sufficed."

What we are now discussing is the quickest of all ways to come quickly to the point. Get rid of the elongated clichés, the necklaces of verbiage, the needless strings of words. This is pruning of a special type. It trims untidy phrases, or lops them off entirely. Why the wasteful "from the standpoint of . . ." when "for" will do the job? Why "within capabilities of the state of the art . . ." when it condenses so neatly to "able"?

Such overadorned verbiage is habit-forming. And "don'ts" alone cannot cure the trouble, because there is no sharp definition of wordiness. The technician may feel content when he substitutes *hence* for *therefore*, but why not go further—to *so*? I knew a writer who cleansed himself of "as a natural matter of fact." It became "as a matter of fact." But why not just "in fact"?

The most obvious fault of the word-chains is in their taking so much space to say so little. An example is the way *case* is overworked. The variations are many. Here are a few:

in case of (*if*)
in many cases (*often*)
in this case (*here*)
in all cases (*always; all*)
In the case of motors we . . . (*For motors we . . .*)
In the case of gases this does not apply (*This does not apply to gases*)

Another example. Economists like to think that their statistics are as crisply no-nonsense as the data of science. But note, in the following droning passage by an economist, that right from the unfortunate first word the passage merely links one useless phrase to another:

> Unfortunately, however, one finds it necessary to add that such comparisons as these belong strictly in the category of what might be described, to borrow from the baseball jargon, "broken bat statistics."

And, of course, textbooks on technology are constantly forcing their readers to struggle with the "It can easily be seen . . ." that is definitely not easy to see.

Such word-wasting is an obvious fault. Less obvious—and even more important—is the service these necklaces perform as camouflage for the writer who doesn't care to come out with a frank "I don't know." For example, the many variations of "not too . . .":

> The estimate was not too accurate. (*Was it inaccurate? Even the horrible* guesstimate *would be more honest.*)

> The scale factor was not too small. (*Small? Medium? Large? Large enough?*)

> The procedure did not seem too costly. (*A bargain? An extravagance? Economically feasible?*)

We should not confuse the worthless phrases with those that perform useful service. Legitimate qualifiers are needed. Transitions (see Chapter 12) are aided by such phrases as "On the other hand" and "In the meantime." We definitely need sharpeners of meaning, such influence phrases as "but only in."

Very useful, too, are what might be called lead-in or "rest" words. They take some space but are worth it. Some like the speaker's "by and large" let the reader catch his breath when the going is heavy: "to sum up"; "in short"; "let me repeat." They are most useful when they show the reader where you are heading: "of course"; "for example"; "it is known that"; "this kind of evidence."

The check-rein on all these should be moderation and usefulness. When they drown the manuscript in verbiage or fog the meaning, they become ripe for purging. In the 175 words on the last page of a horticultural research paper on delphinium breeding, I find these garlands instead of the solid facts that the reader hungers for: "It is interesting to note that"; "This is fortunate inasmuch as"; "Would be highly desirable to have incorporated in"; "It seems to succeed very well in a relatively"; "Are as yet unavailable"; "Almost as susceptible, indicating almost complete dominance"; "The possibility also exists that"; "May prove of value"; "It is evident that."

There is a choice of cures when you detect such anti-simplification in your own writing. If it is a meaningless garland, kill it outright. If it is vague, sharpen its meaning. If it really says something, but too lengthily, chop it down to a suitable word or two. If it sometimes serves a purpose, use it—only sometimes.

The examples above show, in general, what to avoid. Here are specific troublemakers and ways to handle them.

Check-list of Wordy Phrases

("Kill?" indicates phrase probably needs no substitute)

Wordy Phrase	Substitute	Wordy Phrase	Substitute
a great deal of	*much*	as stated pre-	
a majority of	usually *most*	viously	(kill?)
a number of	*many, several*	as to	(kill?)
according to	(kill?)	at much greater	
accounted for by		rates than	*faster*
the fact	*because*	at the present	
after the conclu-		time	*now, at present*
sion of	*after*		(or kill)
along the lines		based on the fact	
of	*like*	that	*because*
along this line	(kill?)	brief in duration	*quick*
as a matter of		came to an end	*ended*
fact	*in fact* (or kill)	case in question	(kill?)
as far as . . . is		connection made	
concerned	*this* (or kill)	by (through)	*connected by*
as long as	*because*		*(through)*

Check-list of Wordy Phrases (*continued*)

consensus of opinion	*opinion, feeling, verdict*	is defined as	*is*
designed to fit	*fits*	is dependent upon	*depends on*
due to the fact that	*because*	is equipped with	*has*
during the time that	*while*	is similar to	*like, resembles*
for the purpose of	*for, to*	it is known that	*we know*
for the reason that	*because*	it is requested	*I ask, will you?* (or kill)
for this reason	*so*	it should be understood	(kill?)
found to be	(kill?)	more specifically	(sharpen)
from the standpoint of	*for*	not as a rule	*not usually*
having regard to	(kill?)	not infrequently	(sharpen)
higher degree of	*higher, more*	not often	(sharpen)
in accordance with	*by, from*	one finds it necessary to	*we must*
in addition to	*also, besides*	one of the reasons	*a reason, one reason*
inasmuch as	*because*		
in case of, etc.	(see examples, page 126)	one of the ways	*one way*
in close proximity	*close, near*	on the part of	(kill?)
in operation	(kill?)	point out	*say, explain*
in order to	*to*	prior to	(only when necessary)
in other words	(kill?)	state of the art	(sharpen or kill)
insofar as	*if*	subsequent to	*after*
in the last analysis	(kill?)	such as	*like*
in terms of	(kill?)	that is to say	(kill?)
in the meantime	*meanwhile*	the foregoing	usually *these, those*
in the neighbourhood of	*about*	the question as to whether	*whether*
		there is reason to believe	*I think*
		this is a subject which	*this*

Check-list of Wordy Phrases *(continued)*

through the use of	*by, with*	with regard to	*concerning, about*
to the facilitation of	*for*	with the exception of	*except*
with a view to	*to, for*	with the result that	*resulted*
with reference to	*concerning about*		

9

EQUATE FOR CLARITY

COMPOSING sentences is more than counting words. Furthermore, with words, you can imagine yourself to be the reader and then judge which words will give him discomfort. With sentences it is better to put yourself in an editor's shoes because the average reader is an unsatisfactory critic. He can only repeat what he tells the doctor about an internal ailment, "It hurts, but I'm not exactly sure where."

Being your own editor—your own diagnostician—need not be at all complicated. There is no obligation to magnify the difficulty. Molière demonstrated this in his satire on syntax.

His play *Le Bourgeois Gentilhomme* derides M. Jourdain, a social climber who is writing an amorous declaration to a noble-woman. He wants to say something along the lines of "Beautiful marchioness, your fair eyes make me die for love." But he wants to say it better. He consults the pedant who has been teaching him culture:

> TEACHER: One may arrange the words first of all as you said. Or
> suppose: "For love die me make, beautiful marchioness, your
> fair eyes." Or perhaps: "Your eyes fair, for love me make,
> beautiful marchioness, die." Or suppose: "Die your fair eyes,

beautiful marchioness, for love me make." Or however: "Me make your eyes fair die, beautiful marchioness, for love."

JOURDAIN: But of all these ways, which is the best?

TEACHER: That which you said, "Beautiful marchioness, your fair eyes make me die for love."

The teacher could have offered a multitude of other permutations and combinations. Permuting is a familiar mathematical practice. It shows 120 different ways to arrange five words and nearly 1,000 ways to arrange six.

Too many writers in science and technology feel betrayed when the one best way is not prescribed. This grows into dislike for writing—its rules are not simple enough. But this is intolerance. It forgets that there are many ways to build a motor car, many ways to moderate the neutron activity in a nuclear pile; that the decision depends on specific needs and the capability of the craftsman.

Science works with mathematical equations. In much the same way word-equations will solve problems of syntax. Just as each word, like a mathematical constant, should have precise meaning, so should each sentence "balance." The method is no more abstruse than applying logic and neatness to the problem of laying flagstones for a terrace.

An example is the rearrangement often necessary when we get snarled in a string of suspensive adjectives.

Wrong: The smoke-stack discharged sulphur, arsenic, antimony and uranium carrying compounds.

Hyphens will correct that but leave it unnecessarily complex

The smoke-stack discharged sulphur-, arsenic-, antimony- and uranium-carrying compounds.

Why so much suspensiveness when the sentence can be recast?

The smoke-stack discharged compounds carrying sulphur, arsenic, antimony and uranium.

Similarly:

Wrong: The satellite will be equipped with cosmic ray, X-ray, ion plasma and meteorite detectors.

Right: The satellite will carry detectors of cosmic rays . . .

Or take the reverse trouble—only one modifier but it seemingly refers to more than one thing.

> *Wrong:* Engineers who appraised the drawing showed a surprising lack of interest and desire to discuss it again. (*A simple sentence but* "surprising lack" *modifies too much.*)

> *Right:* Engineers who appraised the drawing showed a surprising lack of interest, but a willingness to discuss it again. (*What the writer really meant.*)

Sometimes careless equating can leave the reader so badly in the air that he wonders if there is any equation at all.

> *Wrong:* Relaxation is important, not at the end of the day but during.

> *Right:* Relaxation is important, during the day and not at its end.

All troubles with faulty modifiers and antecedents, including those with dangling participles and split infinitives, can be laid at the doorstep of faulty equating.

FAULTY REFERENCES

No matter how short the sentence, it becomes complex when its internal references aren't sharp. The farther apart they are, the worse the equation and the more likely that the sentence will need recasting. The following two examples are short enough—but entirely ambiguous:

> (*a*) This has led to an educational programme started by Californians without precedent. (*The* Californians *aren't without precedent; it's the* programme.)
> (*b*) Another type measures the change in electrical resistance in a wire caused by the deformation. (*Why even hint at the impossible? Surely the deformation doesn't* cause *a wire.*)

In both examples the trouble can be compared to equating like this: $9 = 2 \times (3+3)$.

That answer is wrong. We know that $3+3$ is 6; multiply by 2 and you get 12. The equation should, of course, be: $9 = 2 \times 3 + 3$. Here the 2 multiples only one of the 3's.

In the first sentence, by analogy, *programme* innocently but wrongly "multiplies"—refers to—all that follows. Now let's see what it should refer to. Let's bring *precedent* next to *programme* where it belongs.

> This has led to an *unprecedented* educational *programme* started by Californians.
> *Alternative:* This has led Californians to start an *unprecedented* educational *programme*.

In the second example, the trouble lies in the position of *caused by the deformation*. Again narrow the distance, to establish the true relationship.

> Another type measures the *change* in electrical resistance *caused* by the deformation of a wire.

In both examples the faulty modifier was at end of the sentence. The "squinting modifier" is merely a variation that rests inside the sentence and refers ambiguously to elements on either side. Again the cure is to express the ideas in logical order.

> *Wrong:* The process that incorporates automation in the end is the cheapest.
>
> *Right:* In the end, the process that incorporates automation is the cheapest.

When a sentence is quite long, especially if it is loaded down with qualifying phrases, faulty reference can be cured by the splitting process described in the preceding chapter. Simply sever the sentence at the trouble spot, and add the few words needed.

> *Wrong:* George Ohm was another pioneer whose work on the characteristics of a galvanic circuit led him to the law for determining the flow of an electric current within a conductor. (Whose *is the troublemaker here. Did several pioneers, or only Ohm, do this specific work?*)

If it was Ohm only, then:

> George Ohm was another pioneer in electrical history. His work on the characteristics . . .

If Ohm was one of several, then:

> George Ohm was one of several pioneers who worked on the characteristics of a galvanic circuit. This led to the law for determining . . .

Other times, a long-winded sentence needs vigorous recasting.

> They heard official reports on techniques for taming the power of the hydrogen bomb that might have come out of a modern version of *Alice in Wonderland*.

The grammarian would cite that as a classic case of trouble with antecedents. The pronoun *that* should refer back to the startling facts on techniques. Instead, it seems to say the bomb is coming out of *Alice in Wonderland*.

> *Recast:* They heard reports that revealed techniques for taming the power of the hydrogen bomb. These were official reports. But they sounded so fanciful that they might have come from a modern version of *Alice in Wonderland*.

The words *that* and *which* serve as relative pronouns; so do *who* and *whom*. These pairs are chronic nuisances that I will discuss in the next chapter. For the moment, look back at *that* in the faulty version of the bomb sentence. There, surprisingly enough, *that* is trespassing on the rights of *which* (the trespassing is usually the other way around). Substituting *which* would have been insufficient to cure the trouble.

In the next example, *which* is correct usage but we still have bad equating.

> *Wrong:* He held the crowbar between his knees, which he shook vigorously.

> *Right:* Holding the crowbar between his knees, he shook it vigorously.

> *Right:* He held the crowbar between his knees and shook it vigorously.

Note that substituting *it* for *which* eliminated the confusion. But *it* is not always your guarantee against careless equating.

Wrong: It is a difficult operation because it is not safe to use anesthesia. (*The second* it is *an impersonal one that halts the reader abruptly; he hunts for an antecedent and finds none.*)

Right: It is a difficult operation because anesthesia cannot be used safely.

Wrong: First remove the fuse which is next to the valve and put it in the liquid. It is an operation that must be performed carefully. (*Put what in the liquid?*)

Better: First remove the fuse, which is next to the valve, and put it in the liquid. This operation must be performed carefully. (*The parenthetical commas help* which *refer correctly to* fuse *and the first* it; *being more specific gets rid of the second* it.)

Still better: First remove the fuse (next to the valve) and put it in the liquid. This operation must be performed carefully.

Best: In this operation, which must be performed carefully, first remove the fuse (next to the valve), then put it in the liquid.

The troubles with *it* are echoed with its plural, *they.*

Wrong: The fuses and valves are close together; this is why they cannot be removed easily. (*Remove the fuses, or valves, or both?*)

Right: The fuses cannot be removed easily because they are too near the valves.

Other pronouns need watching too.

Wrong: The important thing about the plane is that he can fold up the wings and roll down the highway. (*Not really! The trouble here is compound: an* it *lacking, and the article* the *where possessive pronouns are needed.*)

Right: The important thing about his plane is that he can fold up its wings and roll it down the highway.

SPLIT INFINITIVES

There is increasing realization that much too much fuss has been made over this sin. The problem too often resembles that of the straw man erected for purposes of mowing him down. Even the purist, after condemning the malpractice, usually goes on to concede that a smooth-sounding split infinitive is preferable to an awkward alternative. But note that there is no virtue in an awkward split infinitive.

The problem merely illustrates the need for common sense. In a sentence-equation, the split infinitive is a modified infinitive. Whether this is good or bad depends on whether or not the modifier is doing its best work.

In the first of the following two examples, the infinitive *to combine* is modified by the adverb *quickly*; in the second, *to avoid* is modified by the adverb *neatly*.

> *Bad:* It is cheaper to combine the prototype stage with the developmental phase quickly.

> *Split:* It is cheaper to quickly combine the prototype stage with the developmental phase.

There, the split infinitive sounds better. Why? In the nonsplit version, *quickly* is a tailpiece—too far away. By placing it where it belongs the meaning is sharpened. The same could be accomplished with *to combine quickly* but our ears tell us this is stilted.

> *Bad:* It was an alternative chosen neatly to avoid the risk.

> *Better:* It was an alternative chosen to avoid the risk neatly.

> *Split:* It was an alternative chosen to neatly avoid the risk.

Why is the third version good? It brings *neatly* back with *to avoid*, where it belongs—a simple formula that snuggles the modifier up to the modified. But doesn't the first do this too? Yes. But it also snuggles *neatly* next to another verb, *chosen*. The result is double meaning. Does *neatly* refer to the method of choosing or the method of avoiding? Splitting the infinitive— sandwiching *neatly* right inside *to avoid*— solves the problem neatly. Some will prefer the second version, which also cures the

K

trouble. Take your choice between the second and third, whichever sounds better. In other words, the split infinitive is not always the only answer. Don't forget ear-satisfying syntax. For example:

> *Bad:* They have decided to build properly the prototype.

> *Bad:* They have decided to properly build the prototype.

> *Good:* They have decided to build the prototype properly.

The first is not idiomatic—it sounds awkward. The second splits the infinitive, but our ears don't like that—they want *prototype* emphasized as much as *to build*. The third is workaday English—and precise too.

Sometimes, of course, you cannot make a clean decision.

> The court requires the patents either to be licensed or relinquished.

> The court requires the patents to be either licensed or relinquished.

There, the first is common usage. The second is also common but it splits the infinitive. One answer is to take your pick. But a better is to simplify.

> The court requires that the patents be licensed or reliquished.

The infinitive is not the only verb form that brings up questions of splitting. Take Abraham Lincoln's "have thus far so nobly advanced." There you can count a string of four qualifying words sandwiched in between two halves of the past participle *have advanced*. Yet we agree it is noble prose.

But take this example of less effective splitting—again that problem of properly building a prototype, but now with a past participle instead of an infinitive:

> They have built properly the prototype.

> They have properly built the prototype.

> They have built the prototype properly.

The first isn't idiomatic; the second splits the past participle but it doesn't sound right nor is the meaning entirely clear; the third is certainly best.

Even when the verb is a kind that cannot be split, similar problems arise—where should the modifier be placed?

The geological formation only has one outstanding characteristic.

The geological formation has only one outstanding characteristic.

This is more specifically the problem of where to place the adverb (see Chapter 7, page 106). In this example the position of *only* isn't important. The second version is considered more literate and is a bit more precise too. But many good writers find the first version clear enough and do not let the problem bother them.

However, when the sentence is more complex, there is more need to move *only* near to whatever it modifies:

Bad: The racing cars will only be expected to drive 500 miles.

Good: The racing cars will be expected to drive only 500 miles.

In the second, I have pried *only* out of the verb *will be expected*. In doing so I avoided splitting the infinitive ("to only drive"). My objective was to place *only* right next to what it should modify, the mileage.

No, there are no infallible rules here. But there are two guide-lines.

▶ Use the equation method—keep modifier and modified close together. This gives clarity.

▶ Use common sense and your ears—the writing should sound English, not uncomfortably stilted or "foreign."

THOSE DANGLERS

Like the split infinitive, the dangling participle and its kin give the grammarian a happy hunting ground. Our interest in them here is strictly functional—what harm they do, and how they can be avoided. Unlike the split infinitive, they can be a serious fault as well as sound inelegant. It is easy enough to recognize them as a special case of the faulty reference.

Sometimes a dangling participle is merely ridiculous.

Being torn to pieces, I had the seat re-covered. (*I wasn't torn to pieces.*)

More often it makes the reader halt abruptly and start a search for the true meaning.

Having missed his plane, the schedule was upset. (The schedule didn't miss the plane.)

Other verb forms can dangle too.

Being torn to pieces is why I had the seat re-covered.

Here, *being* is a gerund instead of a present participle. Both verbals are recognized by their ending in *ing*. But the participle is working as a verb and the gerund is working as a noun—the entire gerund phrase "being torn to pieces" is the subject of "is." This makes little difference to us. The end result is as ridiculous one way as the other. Neither dangling participle nor dangling gerund logically modifies the subject of the principal verb as it should.

Infinitives can dangle too. And so can various elliptical clauses.

While seeking the answer, the question came up again. (*Somebody, unmentioned here, was seeking the answer.*)

Now 51 years old, his hair has begun to grey. (*Argue, if you wish, that his hair is 51 years old, along with the rest of him, but that's quibbling. It is not his hair that is being called 51 years old, but an unnamed true subject—namely* he. *The sentence should read:* "He is now 51, and his hair has begun to grey.")

As a draughtsman Mr. Jones' statements were read by me and found most gratifying. (*I, not Mr. Jones, am the draughtsman:* "I am a draughtsman and I found Mr. Jones' statements most gratifying.")

The rule for the participle is that its phrase must refer unmistakably to a grammatical subject.

Wrong: Watching the fire, it is easy to see why it burns slowly.

   Right: Watching the fire, I can easily see why it burns slowly. (*No doubt here that it's* I *who watch the fire.*)

The rule for all danglers is the same; they should clearly modify the logical subject of the principal verb. It is understandable why the ambiguity caused by dangling gets worse as a sentence becomes more complex—another argument for simpler sentences.

Let us not be too shamefaced in this matter. It is not only the science writer who, by dangling participles and such, ties a sentence in knots. Theodore M. Bernstein, assistant managing editor of the New York *Times*, is an expert's expert in matters of journalistic craftsmanship. In the *Winners & Sinners* sheet that he circulates for the edification and greater skill of that newspaper's reporters and editors, he points happily to specimens of their better work and rails at the other kind. Thus:

> Sitting here on the balcony of a small hotel with a breeze blowing softly off the Aegean Sea below, the college world of New Haven, with its classrooms, its football week-ends and its fraternities, seems eons away.

Bernstein adds this comment: "And its English courses—how far away do they seem?"

Even one of America's most aristocratic presidents, John Adams, was known to dangle on occasion. In his autobiography, he says: "The next morning, I think it was, sitting in my office, near the town house stairs, Mr. Forrest came in."

But remember that our kind of writing must be clear. Whether the dangler does or doesn't make a sentence complex with verbiage, it does introduce ambiguity. That is its big fault. And if you dangle too often, you also acquire a reputation for being uneducated.

FOR CLARITY

What is the cure for all these ambiguities and inelegancies caused by bad positioning? Call in a rule of grammar if you prefer, if you know how to parse a sentence formally—to sort it into its subordinate and independent clauses, its modifying phrases and modified subject, its participles, gerunds and infinitives.

But the trouble is just as curable by examining the sentence to see if it makes logical sense. Is it neatly constructed? In other words, do its elements equate? The cure applies equally to danglers, to split infinitives, to the other faulty modifiers. You do not need an array of rules. The neatness of equating is enough.

You need not be a grammarian, for example, to spot the fact that this editor was on the right track in his effort to tabulate the four points of his magazine's creed, but that he didn't carry the logic far enough:

1. To make all reasonable efforts to ensure accuracy of editorial matter. [*Firm and clear.*]
2. To publish promptly corrections brought to our attention. [*Awkwardly evades a split infinitive.*]
3. To not knowingly publish misleading advertisements. [*Switching to the negative makes this sound like a weak alibi.*]
4. To reserve the right to refuse any advertisement. [*Clear; nicely balances 1.*]

Wouldn't the creed sound better, and be more forceful, too, if the second point split its infinitive: "To promptly publish corrections brought to our attention"? And if the third unsplit its infinitive and turned positive: "To publish no advertisements that we know to be misleading"?

Nor need you be a grammarian to realize that the translator of Jules Verne's *From the Earth to the Moon* was innocently supplying more humour than the French writer intended:

"Ridiculous!" replied Tom Hunter, whittling with his bowie knife the arms of his easy chair. "Ay, and no war in prospect!" continued the famous James T. Maston, scratching with his steel hook his gutta-percha cranium.

10

COMMON USAGE—HOW COMMON?

WE want to understand each other. This is why we share a stock of words and why we try to cement them together in ways that make sense. This is why we wrap up disciplines in what are called rules of writing. Some are ironclad, some flexible, some mistreated, some treacherous. And even the ironclad ones can give trouble.

The equating technique described in the last chapter will rid a sentence of ambiguous modifiers. Common sense will strengthen clarity by simplifying the words and sentences. But what about the many times when we are confronted by a choice between two or more adequately clear answers to a problem? Or a choice between what almost everybody says and what the rules say we should say? Clarity is vital but we want to remain within the accepted standards that govern a reasonably well-educated person.

When either will be clear enough to the reader, should it be "who" or "whom," "that" or "which," "practical" or "practicable," "data is" or "data are"? Should it be "mitosis' stages" or "mitosis's stages"—and is there a better way? Such problems are many.

This chapter is a quick trip into the no man's land of exposition. It first discusses the rules as practical working tools. Then follow two glossaries—of grammar and of vocabulary—showing ways to overcome common troublemakers that I have met as writer, editor and teacher.

Just what is this no man's land? It is the area where rules of writing turn vague, sometimes contradictory, and lead us in circles. Here, when we want neat answers, we hear "yes but's" and "but if's"—and occasionally an exchange of shots between inflexible Grammarians and incorrigible Common Usagers.

An example is that most pathetic of all writing blunders, "between you and I." It's the result of learning a good rule badly or following a misguided notion that "between you and me" sounds inelegant.

Not only is "between you and I" ungrammatical, it is not even idiomatic, and is therefore doubly sinful. Now look at its cousin, "It is I." This is grammatical but it is maladroit because most people, educated as well as uneducated, are more comfortable with "It is me." What should you do? If you are being correct, your choice is the first. Otherwise, you may follow the crowd instead of good grammar and choose "It is me." If that's a sin, your judges are probably guilty too.

But let us go one step farther. Let's take this sentence:

The best danged chemist in the entire company is I.

There, one rule gives you that grammatical but clumsy *I*. Another so-called "rule" puts the more arresting words at the beginning. And yet the sentence sounds terrible.

One answer would be the "It is me" kind, to turn ungrammatical: "The best danged chemist in the entire company is me."

But why not simply come right out and say, "I am the best danged chemist in the entire company"? That is comfortable, and correct too.

What I did there was exercise a writer's privilege. When the rules become difficult, perhaps absurd, don't be the stubborn bull who tries to plunge straight ahead. Go round them. That is the functional, not the theoretical, way to write. It shows awareness of the realities. It is the reason why today's writer is not being made obsolete by computers, translators and other so-called "thinking machines," which can only do what they are programmed to do.

But the realistic approach must be coupled with a strong warning. When you are detouring round a particular problem, you are not escaping the rules of grammar and vocabulary. You are, rather, taking a path that will let you follow a less rigid or more convenient rule. If I haven't formally discussed the rules in this book, it is not because I despise them—in a confused world they do the best they can. It is because: (1) I have been too busy putting them to work in actual situations; (2) this is not a book on grammar, or a dictionary. I must assume that the reader knows the rules or where to find them—or, best, has soaked educated usage into his system through reading and writing.

For writers do learn how to get past the land mines and ambushes of no man's land. Here, for example, an engineer shows confident, correct handling of *that-which* and *who-whom*:

> The one appeal that still works with the bright, sophisticated youngster to whom everything is easy, and who has been brought up in a soft, unresisting environment, is that here is something that is not easy, not soft.

Let's go a bit deeper. Why do the rules fail us? In general, it is because they are either not specific enough or, if sharp, they apologize for exceptions to the rule. And the Oxford English Dictionary urbanely disclaims all liability: "The circle of the English language has a well-defined centre but no discernible circumference."

Even in spelling, even in something supposedly as methodical as the spelling of familiar nouns, why is it "A single mot*or* drives the impell*ers* on the evaporat*or* and conden*ser*" and not "A single mot*er* drives the impell*ors* on the evaporat*er* and condens*or*"?

Very well, let's say spelling lacks logic. Surely frosty-eyed grammar can be depended on for ironclad rules. But we are soon wondering with Mark Twain whether a bluejay or a cat uses better grammar.

What, for example, can you do about the confusion of *shall-will*? Both words sound and look equally good. The rules concerning them have never been clear. These rules have been ignored so much by fine writers and orators that they are now hardly more than museum pieces.

Another example. "Your present love are true and honourable" is a blunder that can be dismissed because it's written in a Chinese fortune biscuit. But what about more complex trouble, such as with *each other*? Singular or plural—and how do you form the possessive?:

The zoologist and the biologist will visit each other's home.

That is technically incorrect because grammar interprets *each other* as a reciprocal pronoun, plural in its meaning; and as a possessive it equals *their*. Hence: *each other's homes*. Correct, but rather stifling, isn't it? That's why the experienced writer dodges:

Each of them, the zoologist and biologist, will visit the other's home.

Now let's take a familiar example of comma trouble:

By this method, metal can be barely warmed or blasted with a power intensity that will cause even tungsten to boil.

The sentence looks grammatical but that's deceptive. Let's see where the true meaning has been lost—why the sentence equates badly. Reading it aloud shows the trouble spot. Punctuation is needed at the word *or* because the contrast is not between *warmed* and *blasted*; it's between *barely warmed* and all that follows. A comma after *warmed* will do; a dash, by emphasizing the contrast, is much better:

By this method, metal can be barely warmed—or blasted with a power intensity that . . .

And what of the less complex troubles? What, for example, is it that leads so many to write: "The company has announced their plan . . ."? Why *their*? It is a company competing with *its* rivals, each of whom is *it*. Here's the old collective-noun pitfall, troublesome both in England and America. It is discussed on page 152 in the glossary of grammar problems.

Simplest of all, what about abbreviations? From the data of science it is not far to the statistics of economics. Both feel the influence of fast-stepping "business English." One result is space-saving carried to extremes. The rules of abbreviation are quite lenient, and "day" becomes the hardly worthwhile "da." "The sailors brought 500 gallons aboard" becomes an alarming "The sailors brought 500 gals aboard." And "15 min min" leaves us groggy. Setting up a subrule that *minutes* equals *min.* (with the period) and *minimum* equals *min* (without the period) would give nothing better than "15 min. min"; here, why not forego the right to abbreviate? Why not "15 minutes minimum"?

Apparently, then, the rules are not entirely to blame. Let us agree that we sometimes confuse the reader with carelessness, bad judgment and barbarisms that could be avoided. Realizing this, we can now speak more plainly about the rules as tools for the workman.

USAGE: HOW COMMON?

The so-called "rules" of writing are those preached and usually practiced by good writers and by teachers of writing. Though loosely called the rules of grammar, they also cover the good manners of spelling and the other mechanistic formalities. For example, one rule that has come to be generally accepted is: The comma or period goes inside, not outside, the closing quotation mark.

And there is the simplest "rule" of all: Be a neat housekeeper. Though usually considered too plebeian to be mentioned among the more literary injunctions, this one carries unchallengeable weight. It warns you when to put in a fresh typewriter ribbon if you type, to cross your *t*'s and dot your *i*'s if you write, to leave space on the paper for editing, and so on. Overlooking this rule violates the first requirement of writing: Remember the reader (who, with manuscript, is usually an editor). It's surprising how many authors put their worst foot forward when they write, how many arouse prejudice against their paper by offering it in an untidy state.

The more complicated rules of grammar and rhetoric bring up problems that are harder and often controversial. Is it "a number of men *is*" or a number of men *are*"? When may you split an infinitive with impunity? How slangy have you a right to be? Just who has the right to decide such matters?

We do surmise that despite its frequent lawlessness, language has a supreme court. Nobody knows where it sits, and its justices are imaginary. Yet it cannot be entirely a myth, because its dictums are forever being offered as proof of something or other. It's called Common Usage.

The trouble lies in the question: Whose Common Usage?

Some writers prefer the usage of today's educated people, much of which, once upon a time, was the usage of rather common folk. It evolved. Others prefer the lowly but fresh language of right now, and of tomorrow when it comes. Some purists prefer Anglo-Saxon roots, others dig back to old Greece and Rome. The spectrum of Common Usage is therefore extremely wide, and made up of many bands. Even those who call scientists "eggheads" have to differentiate between the writing of subgroups dubbed "longhairs" and "crewcuts."

One of the attempts at simplification has been made by Robert Burger, research editor at Amos Tuck School, Dartmouth. He offers a breakdown of three main types:

Anarchists. They believe it doesn't matter how you say it as long as you're understood.

Schoolmarms. The wince at colloquialisms, shudder at slang, and so forth.

Grammarians. They accept only the rules that make sense, serve a purpose, and enrich the language.

It would be hard not to side with such grammarians. For however fascinated you might be by the libertines, anarchism is not for our field. So forget it. Our common usage is that of the educated person, not of the crossroads beer parlour or the student who hasn't time to consult grammar. And schoolmarmism is overdone too. An example is the report that predicts juvenile delinquency in the child who says "ain't." Or listen to this letter from a young student to a successful author:

I am interested in paragraph writing. Can you answer these questions. When should you start paragraph writing? When should you start a book? I hope you will write another book about dinosaurs.

Apparently paragraph-writing was still out of bounds for that poor kid sentenced to writing sentences—an illustration of the trouble with strait-jacket methods, which forget that rules are always inchoate, always developing. The rules can sum up the standards of good writing but they can write nothing.

Nor can they function unless we supply common sense when we run into trouble. Even Fowler's masterpiece, let's admit it, is less helpful for fast references than as a book for browsing through, delightful browsing as the British scholar switches from now a yelp to now a groan while he is wrestling with barbarisms.

Standard dictionaries, special ones such as Fowler's, and the textbooks on grammar and rhetoric—these are the repositories of common usage that serve as rule books.

With only a standard dictionary, the usual writer can get by. With that plus a competent book on grammar, a thesaurus, perhaps also a compilation of quotations and a stylebook for stylisms (see Chapter 15, page 230), you can do quite well. These are your tools.

PRACTICAL PATH

But nobody can supply a sound rule for every occasion. So, for the rest—when you find yourself in no man's land—you must fall back on your common sense. Yes, know the rules, because they were framed to help you and they do bend to meet changing needs. Distinguish between those that always make sense and those that aren't rules at all. And when you must depart from an accepted rule, or if you sometimes wish merely to kick up your heels a bit, remember that you will be judged by how far you wander.

In a charming defence of culture and good manners, *The New Yorker* put it this way:

> The living language is like a cowpath: it is the creation of the cows themselves, who, having created it, follow it or depart from it according to their whims or their needs. From daily use, the path undergoes change. A cow is under no obligation to stay in the narrow path she helped make, following the contour of the land, but she often profits by staying with it and she would be handicapped if she didn't know where it was and where it led to. Children obviously do not depend for communication on a knowledge of grammar; they rely on their ear, mostly, which is sharp

and quick. But we have yet to see the child who hasn't profited from coming face to face with a relative pronoun at an early age, and from reading books, which follow the paths of centuries.

The problem of singular-plural agreement between subject and verb is typical. Let's apply the principle of freedom to wander:

The "Big 3" has shortened the wheel base in their new-model cars.

If you decide that "Big 3" is singular, a unitized trio, then subject and verb agree, but the rest should agree too: *its* new-model cars. But you don't like that. So you try the plural: "The 'Big 3' *have* shortened the wheel base in their new-model cars." But again you feel uncomfortable. This cowpath is taking you nowhere, so you turn off into another. You recast the sentence. It now turns passive, but you will be forgiven for breaking the so-called rule against passivity:

The wheel base *has been shortened* in the new-model cars of the "Big 3."

Now there is no longer need to decide whether "*Big 3*" is singular or plural. *Wheel base* is definitely singular. But was all this necessary? There could have been agreement, and the sentence could have remained active. Here was a third path:

Each of the "Big 3" *has* shortened the wheel base in *its* new-model cars.

Common Trouble-makers—Grammar

Possessive. The problem that arouses most discussion here is the one that's least important. To indicate the genitive, do you add '*s* to a noun already ending in *s*? That is, do you write "Charles' tonsils" or "Charles's tonsils"? Many, like me, prefer the former. Your best guide is your editor. The way he likes it—give it to him that way.

But the possessive cannot always be dismissed so lightly. Even Gertrude Stein has written the apostrophe often. Her explanation: "I find myself letting it alone if it has come in and sometimes it has come in."

How can the apostrophe be directed to the right place? When may it simply be thrown away?

▶ In *Adam Bede*, a pair of cousins are named Bess. To identify them, the villagers added the names of the fathers. One young woman became "Chad's Bess"; the other, "Timothy's Bess." When the latter bore a son, he was called "Timothy's Bess' Ben."

An agile writer need not be caught that way. He remembers that the simple preposition *of* can also indicate the possessive. Just as he would write "Ben, the son of Timothy's Bess," if need be, he gets around tongue-twisting "electroluminescence's limitations" with "limitations of electroluminescence."

▶ The same detour often gives a happy ending to more aggravated problems than "Charles's tonsils." I prefer "mitosis' stages" to "mitosis's stages." But neater yet is "stages of mitosis."

▶ Another way, which works nicely with inanimate objects, is to delete any outward sign of possession. Make it simply "the TV aerial" (not "the TV's aerial").

▶ With plurals a handy answer is the "three-minute-egg formula." Of the following three examples, all are correct, but the first is simplest—*a 10-minute flight, a 10 minutes' flight, a flight of 10 minutes.*

▶ A special and treacherous nuisance is *its-it's*. It's *its* when *it* possesses something. The *it's* is simply a contraction for *it is*. Yet even on the jacket of a book, I find a city being described: "It's Growth, It's Decay, It's Future."

Prepositions. To paraphrase Carl Becker, if ending a sentence with a preposition leads to absolute ruin, then all I can say is that absolute ruin is what it leads to. But other prepositional faults do cause mischief.

▶ Don't confuse liberty with license. Don't, by writing the way you speak, perpetrate a sentence such as this one heard at a congressional session: "Medical journals are almost notorious for being easy to get into."

▶ Make sure that the preposition is idiomatic: different *from* (not *than*); independent *of* (not *from*); in search *of* (not *for*); pleased *with* (not *by*).

▶ Avoid recasting a phrase when the result is clumsy. Even the "creative head" at a mammoth advertising agency feels embarrassed when he's called "head of creation."

▶ Don't let prepositions pile up. Example: "The temperature will rise to from between about 75 and 85 degrees F to between about 150 and 175 degrees F." That indicates the writer is uncertain about his facts. I think it means: The temperature will first rise to 75-85 degrees F, then go up to 150-175 degrees. Or: The temperature will first reach a range of 75 to 85 degrees F, then go up to the range of 150-175.

Singular or plural. Why does it sound odd when the translator of Jules Verne writes, "This accident cost the *life* of several workmen"?

We would write, ". . . cost the *lives* of several workmen." But we would also write, "the *price* of today's cars" instead of "the *prices* of today's cars."

In choosing we are being safely guided by sweet reason, by our ability to count, and by what sounds idiomatically correct. These three save us from giving the wrong number when the rules are complicated, even contradictory. And of the three it is often idiom that decides.

The distinction between singular and plural is hardest with so-called collective nouns—not only *committee, panel, majority, group,* but such other examples as *company* and *corporation.* The first four make sense either way, depending on what you mean. Examples: "The majority (sing.) cast *its* vote for a biologist"; "The majority (plu.) *are* biologists." The choice depends on whether you mean the group as a whole (sing.) or individuals in the group (plu.).

But it's odd to think of an industrial company as plural. Example: "The company has announced expansion of *their* steel production." This sounds pompously much like a king saying "We" for "I." This isn't a company of Chaucer's pilgrims, each telling a story, each with his or her own characteristics. Even a company of soldiers is more often "it." The industrial company should be *it*; therefore, *its* plans, *its* production, *its* rivals. Now go back to the original. That writer was apparently playing it both ways: singular *has* with plural *their.* This definitely is not allowed. If you really mean the individuals in the company, your only choice is "The company *have* announced expansion of *their* steel production." But it's easier to stay with "The company *has*"; "The group *says*"— and usually more accurate.

Note: the collective *number* is a special problem for which we usually have a special and easy guide. Let the article decide. *The* takes singular: *a* takes plural. Example: *The* number of physicists *is* increasing. *A* number of physicists *are* represented.

But what about the more usual troubles, when the verb's subject is not a collective noun? The reasoning is much the same. You write "Cosmic rays *is* (not *are*) the timely topic of tonight's meeting" and "36 kilowatts *is* (not *are*) needed here" because you are thinking collectively. You are bundling those rays and that power together, not thinking of each ray or each kilowatt.

The rule that matters is this. Subject and verb must agree in number. But sometimes agreement doesn't come easily.

1. Is the subject singular or compound? Often you must make a choice. For example, research is one thing, development is a later stage. So you can count them as two different things. As such, they form a compound subject and take a plural verb. Example: "Research and development *have* become a modern-day team." More often, however, they are considered a continuum. Example: "Research and development *is* the first requirement for success."

2. Who is the subject? It's easy to be deceived by the noun closest to the verb. Example: "The date of the sessions *were* postponed a week." But *of the sessions* merely modifies the true subject, *date*. There can be no choice. The sentence must read: "The date of the sessions *was* postponed a week." Here we can see an argument for simpler sentences. The farther a subject is from its verb, the more risk of a wrong countdown. Example: A *liquid* composed of quickly evaporating solvents and two corrosion-proof solutes that will protect the steel girders *have been* ordered. (No matter how many plural nouns in between, *liquid* is the subject and it's singular: ". . . *has been* ordered.")

3. Delayed subject. Example: "There *is* also a large lab., a small supply room, and several committee rooms." *There* only paves the way for the true subject, which is compound and comes after the verb, not before. The sentence should read: "There *are* also a

L

large lab. . . ." Or else supply a genuine subject at the beginning: "The building consists of a large lab., a small supply room . . ."

4. "More than one." Example: "He found that *more than one* leak *was* responsible." Technically, it should be *were responsible.* Actually, *was responsible* is good usage, an example of the rule being wrong, your ear being right.

5. "None." Nobody has a solid answer to this one. You can often sidestep with "no one is." Otherwise, take your pick, "none is" or "none are." But common sense warns that you cannot choose both singular and plural for the same sentence. Wrong: "None of them *was* correct *answers.*" Right: "None of them *was* the correct *answer*" or "None of them *were* correct *answers.*"

6. "Either-neither." When the subject is an "either-or" or "neither-nor" pair, one of its halves may be singular and the other half plural. What, then, does the verb do? Example: "Neither he nor the older members of the institute have spoken." That sentence is correct. The verb (*have spoken*) is plural because it takes the number of the alternative nearest to it (*older members*). If this answer sounds awkward, then dodge. Examples: "Neither he nor any older *member* of the institute *has spoken*"; "Like himself, the *older members* of the institute *have not spoken.*"

Tense. Giving the right time is mainly a matter of equating. Rope-skipping children sing, "I like to play with tools; I like to go to the moon." That, of course, indicates they frequently visit the moon. Our writing can be as perplexing.

1. Tense must accurately tell when something is happening. Here, the rules may sound confusing, and there is so much bad usage around us that our ears cannot be trusted. The only answer is common sense—remembering always just where you are. Right: "He confirmed that antibodies exist"; "He confirms that antibodies exist." Wrong: "He confirmed that antibodies existed" (they still do). Right: "Du Pont announced that it intends to build . . ." (a recent announcement; construction hasn't begun yet). Also right: "Du Pont announces that it intends to build . . ." (again, construction is still to come). But wrong: "In 1929, Du Pont announced that it intends to build . . ." Right: "In 1929, Du Pont announced that it intended to build . . ."

2. To indicate that its news is fresh, the journalism of broad-

casting frequently confuses the listener by giving him wrong time. A script says, "It has been announced this morning that the company will produce tranquilizers." There is no excuse for this has-been, this present-perfect tense, this bringing a finished action into the present. Two more examples: "The President has announced this morning that he will . . ."; "The satellite has been heard from this noon." The mix-up in both is the same. Already-finished action is brought up into present perfect and then made ridiculous with a definite time. The second should be changed to: "The satellite was heard from this noon" (or "was heard from today," or "was heard from two hours ago"). Or else make no claim to definiteness. Clearly show the present perfect: "The satellite has been heard from." One more example shows why *yet* is such a nuisance. Example: "I didn't do the research yet." *Yet* must bring the reader right into the present: "I haven't done the research yet"; "The research is not done yet." *As yet*, besides being no cure, might stress the alibi aspect.

3. Sentences thrown into the subjunctive mood by *if* give special trouble. Example: "All would have used that formula if they thought it worked." This needs the conditional sense of "maybe." It should read: "All would have used that formula if they thought it would work." (More formally it could read: "All would have used that formula if they had thought it would work." Still more formally: "Had they thought it would work, all would have used that formula.")

4. In general, don't let sentimentality for the past cloud your logic. Example: "Years ago when the mark of a Westerner was not how he holds [should be *held*] his guitar but how he holds [should be *held*] his liquor . . ."

Common Trouble-makers—Vocabulary

Some of the words in the list below are indigenous to science writing. Others are confusing words that we share with writers in other fields. The list is not complete but it does cover the words that seem to give most trouble. And it illustrates how easy it is to go astray when words sound alike or are accepted without our examining their true meaning.

Affect—effect. First remember that *affect* rarely can be a noun but *effect* is common. Example: "The effect (result) was higher temperature." Next remember that both *effect* and *affect* can be verbs. Examples: "Heat *affected* (influenced) the choice of motor"; "Heat *effected* (accomplished) a breakdown in the equipment." But *effect* as verb is usually stilted; why not switch to a substitute like *cause*? "Heat *caused* a breakdown . . ."

Among—between. The rule here is hard to justify and has been weakened by many violations—too much *between*, not enough *among*. But to demonstrate literacy, better try to observe the rule: *between* only for two things; *among* for more than two. Examples: "The difference *between* hot and cold"; "The choice *among* metals." Again clarity is paramount. Example: "He chose *among* the several types of transistors"; but "He laid insulation *between* the rows" (or "every two rows") "of transistors."

Answer—solution (as synonyms). The word *answer* is often safer where a problem is concerned, unless you use the verb form—"*solve* a problem." This is because *solution* invites ambiguity when writing about liquids. Example: "The *solution* is an enriched form of maple sap." Does that mean an enriched liquid or solution to a problem? The difficulty vanishes with: "The *answer* is an enriched form of maple sap."

As—like. The rules frown on the "slovenly" use of *like* as a conjunction. But we see violations everywhere. Example (from a professor): "Today's engineer should know economics, just like he should know the simple arts of English prose." Example (from the New York *Times*): "He brought the big ship into the lock like she was an automobile entering a narrow garage."

Those *likes* should jar your ear. If they do, learn the rule. It's simple enough. When you make a comparison, *like* is the preposition. It goes with a noun or pronoun: "behaving *like* children." *As* is the conjunction. It goes with a clause: "just *as* he should know the simple arts of English prose."

Whatever you do, don't go to the other extreme and become ungrammatically elegant: "They behaved as children."

Assure—insure—ensure. We are constantly writing the first or second when we mean the third. By careful handling you *ensure* (make quite] certain) that the transplant will live. You aren't *insuring* (money back if it dies) or *assuring* (promising somebody). True, the dictionary allows some interchangeability; true, a time-honoured insurance company calls itself Equitable Life Assurance Society. But let's stick to precision.

Because—since. The difference here matters more than you may think. Be sure that *since* doesn't start the reader counting time when it's *because* you really mean. It is quite all right to say: "*Since* he was coming anyway, I changed my plan." There, *since* is interchangeable with *because*. But this is bad: "*Since* the first flight of an aeroplane freed man from gravity, it created a new dimension." Clarified: "*Because* the first flight of an aeroplane . . ." Or, recasting: "The first flight of an aeroplane created a new dimension *because* . . ."

Between—among. (see *among*).

Both. This is a good influence word, but it often pops up in a bad place. Example: "It powers both traction rollers and the cutting unit."

Though good-enough grammar, that sounds like two traction rollers, which the writer didn't mean. So he should swerve round the problem. Here are possibilities: "It powers the traction rollers and cutting unit"; "It powers both the cutting unit and the traction rollers"; "It powers the traction rollers and also the cutting unit."

Can—may. Unlike *as* versus *like*, the problem here isn't simply one of bad grammar. The poaching of *may* upon the rights of *can* destroys your meaning and leads to some of the worst confusion in science. Do you mean *could* or *might, has the ability to* or *is permissible?* Example: "Electric components may use liquid semiconductors."

Is this a possibility for the future? Or is it something the components are able to do now? Most likely the latter, but *may* doesn't say that. A simple rule: *may* is the *maybe* word; *can* is the *can-do* word. (Also see Chapter 3, page 39.)

Compare with—compare to. In science we are forever making comparisons *with* but writing *to*. In general, the first compares relative values, the second reaches out for an analogy. You compare the atomic weight of aluminium *with* that of iron; you compare an atom *to* the solar system.

Data is—data are. Inasmuch as the singular is unquestionably *datum*, should we write *data is* or *data are*? Neither confuses us, so this is more a matter of propriety than of clarity. It is unlike the problem of *basis*, for which the plural is *bases*, and that does give trouble. Example: "Bases of the Army's new firepower . . ." If we didn't know the basis for *bases*, we would erroneously be thinking of Army establishments.

Most of us now ignore the existence of *datum*. Instead of "these data *are*" we write "this data is" (plu.) as confidently as we write "this piece of data is" (sing.).

Due to. Misused as well as overused, this phrase should refer only to a noun. What we really mean, most of the time, is the more elegant *owing to* or less elegant *on account of*. But don't worry if you can't pin down the somewhat stuffy difference; all three have earned a bad reputation. You can usually solve everything with the no-nonsense substitute *because*. Example: "The plant froze because of carelessness."

Effect—affect (see *affect*).

Factor. Much overused, this word therefore has become weary and dull. If you mean "one of the causes," then say that instead of "one of the factors."

Feature. This is overworked, like *factor* (with which it's frequently confused). Get a sharper noun. And also spurn it as a verb. A movie uses a colloquialism when it *features* its leading actor, but your experiment doesn't *feature* a new approach; it *reveals, displays, emphasizes, introduces* or even *highlights*.

Flexible—versatile. Engineers, especially, have the confusing habit of calling a rigid object *flexible* when they really mean it's *versatile*—can do several things.

However. At the beginning of a sentence, this word can have two quite different meanings. When it must be followed immediately by a comma, be sure to supply one. Example: "However, discouraging the experiment was not easy." Here, *however* means *but*. When it is not followed by a comma, its meaning is quite different. Example: "However dicouraging the experiment, they did not lose hope." Here, *however* means *no matter how*.

Involved. Watch out for this one. Do you really mean *implicated, entangled*? Or, more likely, do you mean *has joined, is connected with, require,* etc.? Wrong: "He is involved in a project." Right: "He is connected with a project." Wrong: "The results involve statistical analysis." Right: "The results require statistical analysis."

Like—as (see *as*).

Like (meaning *such as*). In this sense, *like* is a word-saver and simplifier. Why be limited to: "This is characteristic of such light metals as magnesium, aluminium and titanium?" You can frequently do better with: "This is characteristic of light metals like magnesium, aluminium and titanium."

Material. This is usually a safe word, but not in technology, where writing is rife with "material advantages," "material benefits," "material needs," when the writers really mean "advantages of the material," "benefits of the material," and so on.

May—can (see *can*).

Now—presently. Only *now* means right now, this moment. *Presently* is another affectation that happens to be wrong. (For more, see Chapter 6, page 94.)

Obvious. This word is good when it saves needless repetition, but it can also be a cowardly word, when the not-so-obvious is being offered instead of the needed facts. To write "obvious advantages" is no better than "well-known advantages" when the advantages are neither obvious nor well known.

Only. Like *both*, this is a valuable word, but sometimes, through nobody's fault, it weakens or wrecks your meaning. The cure is to shift its position in the sentence; the closer to the word or phrase it's supposed to modify, the better. Note how the position of *only* changes the meaning of these two sentences: "We will only try to land on Venus"; "We will try to land only on Venus."

Optimum. It doesn't mean wonderful, superlative. If you mean the best possible compromise, why not say so? If you prefer optimum in that sense, then do not also use it to mean "tops." Instead, switch to such words as *best* and *maximum*.

Or. Trying to help the reader can end in confusing him. Suppose you write "protons" and then, to elucidate, you add "or positively charged particles." But the reader is being misled when he reads "Protons or positively charged particles are able to . . ."

He thinks that both are able to. Here, the *or* phrase is parenthetical. It should be flanked by parentheses or by two commas: "Protons, or positively charged particles, are able to . . ."

Or try some other way: "Protons, which are positively charged particles, are able to . . ."; "The positively charged particles called protons are able to . . ."

Partly—partially. Probably most technicians prefer *partially*. It does sound a bit more elegant. One thing wrong with it is its dangerous nearness to *partial* and *impartial*; it can be confused with prejudice. Aside from that, why not take the simpler way? *Partly* means the same thing.

Practical—practicable. Again, elegance seduces many into the wrong choice. The difference is important. Is a process feasible (*practicable*) or already successful (*practical*)?

Principle—principal. Besides consulting the dictionary, remember that if it's the adjective *principal* you really mean, you can save space with a handy substitute. The word *main*, most likely, is all you need.

Shall—will. Scholars mourn, but Winston Churchill said, "We shall fight on the beaches," and General Douglas MacArthur said, "I shall return." The best thing to do with this hopeless problem is to ignore it. One writer's *will* shall be another writer's *shall*, and let's busy ourselves with things that really matter.

Since—because (see *because*).

Solution—answer (see *answer*).

That—which. Many words have been written about these two bewildering relative pronouns. Many, if not most, writers don't know the difference or don't care. If you do care and don't want to investigate the difference between "restrictive" and "nonrestrictive," remember that four times out of five, or more, it's *which* that trespasses on *that*. Many more of us write the incorrect "The causes which result in a scientific discovery" than write the correct "The causes that result in a scientific discovery."

Or just remember this guide. A *that* clause is one that the sentence cannot do without and still make worthwhile sense. Example: "It was the only process that gave steel cheaply." But a *which* clause is like one in parentheses. Example: "It was a new and important process which gave steel cheaply." In fact, one test is to add the parentheses mentally. Example: "It was a new and important process (which gave steel cheaply)."

While—although. The trouble here, as with *since*, is that the reader may start counting time when the writer only meant *although*, *but* or even just *and*.

Examples of bad usage: "Formerly, science was taught by the textbook method, while [should be *but*] now the laboratory method is favoured"; "While [should be *although*] the spectrum shows the presence of strontium, other tests work faster"; "Stainless steel is one alloy while [should be *and*] bronze is another."

Who—whom. Rules have broken down here, as with *that—which*, but the laws of literacy are enforced more strongly. For one thing, common sense tells you more clearly what to do. The equation method described in Chapter 9 works easily. Example: "This is the man who said, 'I cannot succeed' "; "This is the man of whom it was said, 'He cannot succeed.' "

Both are correct. *Who* is a subject, *whom* is an object. That is, *who* does something, something is done to *whom*.

Yet we constantly see sentences like this: "The doctor *who* I heard at the meeting . . ." That is as illogical as: "The doctor *whom* heard me at the meeting . . ." Correct: "The doctor *whom* I heard at the meeting . . ."; "The doctor *who* heard me at the meeting . . ."

And if in doubt still, remember that good writers outflank bad situations. You could discard both *who* and *whom* and safely say: "The doctor I heard at the meeting . . ."

Will—shall (see *shall*).

11

OH, FOR A GOOD LEAD!

"MOST scientists would rather start work on a new project than write a report about the one they have just completed." —J. Bennett Hill, Director, Research & Development Dept., Sun Oil Co.

That statement can easily be broadened. It applies not only to the project report but to the college theme or thesis, to the magazine article, to the application for a patent, to the job résumé, to the advertising brochure, to almost any expositional chore in our field. It applies to the professional and the amateur—in this they are brothers. And with both, it is the beginning that is troublesome. The amateur's plaint is "Oh, how to start!" The experienced writer phrases it in his own way, "Oh, for a good lead!"

The main difference is that the craftsman knows better what a proper lead should have, and is more willing to toss false starts into the waste-paper-basket until he gets what he wants. And what does he want? He wants to catch the reader's attention, and he wants to keep it. So, if he is a news writer, he settles on:

Air Force scientists will reach up 100 miles over White Sands, New Mexico, early Saturday morning and try to catch some stardust.

If he is writing a thoughtful magazine article:

Today's scientist faces a frank, perhaps brutal question. Is he an honest man? Or are his methods and findings influenced unduly by the desire for fame and fortune?

If he is writing a more leisurely research paper:

> Man is rather philosophical about the hair growing on his face and has even found some ornamental and practical uses for it. His attitude toward the kind of crystals we call whiskers has had a different history. For several centuries science regarded the hairlike filaments as freaks. They were usually considered mineral substances that had somehow taken a bizarre and fragile shape.
>
> Even in more recent years nothing valuable was suspected in these crystals. Quite the contrary . . .

Superficially, in writing style, in length, those three leads are vastly different. But this seeming difference comes from each writer's remembering the commandment: Know your reader.

Each audience is different but each lead is as genuine as the other. Each comes after a title that has stopped the reader—but only momentarily. Now the lead must shoulder the burden. It must "sell" the reader. While he is reading the first paragraph or two, the first 10 to perhaps as many as 150 words, he decides whether to go on—or flip to another title, another book, another proposal, or another memo in the "to be read" pile.

To persuade him, each of the above leads was carefully tailored, so carefully that the beginner is easily deceived into thinking the secret lies in "flowery language." Good writing yes, but flowers no. Each writer remembered that his lead must be accurate—without becoming deadly. It must say much—without being cluttered. And it must in some way describe the content of the entire piece, and also give its flavour.

This is why, when an editor lacks time to do more with a weak manuscript, he tries at least to make the lead workmanlike.

How, then, are good leads written?

Suppose you are well-armed with a bundle of 4 x 6 file cards, or a handful of scribbled notes, or even a good outline; with fresh typewriter ribbon, good lighting and privacy; perhaps also with sandwiches, coffee, chewing gum and other props. Your working tools—vocabulary, punctuation, grammar—are adequate. And still you can't get started. How do you begin covering that paper with your message?

More than with any other phase of writing, rigid rules here are not enough. Leads are too varied. Moreover, the usual textbook doesn't go into details about leads; it takes for granted that to write, you begin somehow. It's a pity that more leading writers of nonfiction don't write books on how to write—specifically, how *they* write. The most rewarding section would be "How I Begin."

At any rate, we can turn to examples. By recognizing the elements in good leads written by others, you prepare to write good ones yourself. Let's figuratively roll up our sleeves and see how an effective lead meets three related requirements. It must:

Persuade. Its style and content must be arresting, must entice the reader to want more. (In advertising, it must be doubly so: Persuade him to read, persuade him to buy.)

Summarize. Whether it's actually the formal summary for a technical paper, or the newspaperman's lead, it must quickly indicate to the reader what the rest will be about.

Lean forward. It cannot tell all in its few words. But it can contain unanswered questions and unfinished answers that will lead the reader on.

The three examples above fulfil the requirements. They waste no time; they quickly offer something interesting. Each, in its own way, gives a preview of what is to follow. And it whets your appetite for more: What's this about catching stardust? Who is accusing today's scientists, and why? What value has been found in those whiskers?

Now let's turn to two great historical documents, and we find the same thing. They quickly tell what they're talking about, and promise interesting details.

These are the times that try men's souls.

That's from Thomas Paine's *The American Crisis*. There, in the first sentence of his lead, he announces the theme and gives the flavour of his call for resistance. The Declaration of Independence, a few months earlier, began with this more grandiloquent paragraph:

> When, in the Course of human events, it becomes necessary for one people to dissolve the political bands which have connected them with another, and to assume among the powers of the earth, the separate and equal station to which the Laws of Nature and of Nature's God entitle them, a decent respect to the opinions of mankind requires that they should declare the causes which impel them to the separation.

There, the need for self-justification swelled the single-sentence lead to 71 words. But again, the writer has come to the point. You can almost imagine a colon at the end of that paragraph; Thomas Jefferson will soon be listing those grievances.

That the fundamentals of all good leads are the same can be illustrated this way. Take the same subject and give it different treatments. You will find this to be valuable practice; and if you want to be a successful freelance, writing for different types of magazines, you will be varying leads as a matter of course.

In the following examples, note how each type of reader has been given an inventory, and in a way that makes him want to read on.

1. For one type of popular magazine:

> Not the surgeon's knife, not the destroying rays of radioactive isotopes—but the self-healing processes of the body itself. This is the radically new approach that science is taking to the conquest of cancer. The goal is an effective vaccine.

2. For another type of popular magazine—a bit more formal:

> Cancer does not throw a fearsome mushroom into the sky but the disease has given us almost as much dread as has the H-Bomb. Part of our fear has come from the resistance of this disease to various treatments. Even such drastic countermeasures as the surgeon's knife and the therapy of radiation are often helpless against the malignant growth; moreover, they themselves endanger the human body. Is it possible that we have been overlooking our strongest ally—the body itself? In other words, what are the prospects for vaccinating against cancer?

3. For a project proposal:

The surprising ability of the human body to manufacture anti-bodies effective against even so malignant an enemy as cancer is the subject of one of the research projects proposed by our staff in this month's programme report.

4. For a research paper:

This investigation was undertaken to learn what natural defences the human body can marshal against cancer. Specifically, we studied the role played by antibodies in repulsing carcinogenous intruders. Results of this two-year study at XYZ Laboratory show conclusively that the formation of anti-cancer antibodies can be stimulated in human subjects. Combining this with other evidence strengthens our belief that medical research is now ready to undertake the task of producing a suitable vaccine that will inhibit or destroy carcinogenous tumours.

All four versions follow the simple dictates of clear writing, which are vital in a lead. Muscle-bound words have been avoided and the jargon level has been adjusted to suit the reader's knowledge of medicine. In the popular versions (1 and 2), reference is made to vaccines—a popular word and adequate for the lead; no need to talk of antibodies just yet. In the more technical leads (3 and 4), antibodies are mentioned at once. But even in 4, note the reference to cancer first, then to carcinogenous intruder, before we go full blast into *carcinogenous tumours*.

Simultaneously, "rules" have not been allowed to cripple the writing. Certainly, shorter sentences are usually preferable; but in these leads, some sentences are short, some long, depending only on the writer's style and desire for effectiveness. Nor were syllables counted. Words were judged by two criteria. Are they precise? Are they clear to this type of reader?

If jargon was avoided, so was the other extreme. The beginner errs hugely, and wastes much time, when he hunts flowery or noisy attention-getters for the lead. Ours is not writing for society columns or tabloids. Our words must be interesting because they say so much—without sacrificing accuracy. Note that none of the four examples proclaims a "cancer cure." It is only the careless amateur who believes popular writing must be "jazzed up." Even the cliché *dread disease* was avoided. The word *dread* appears in 2 but in a fresh, not a shopworn, way.

Such tactics would, of course, be effective in succeeding paragraphs too. The point here is that each lead meets the three requirements: It's persuasive—uncluttered with details that can come later; it summarizes—lets the reader judge whether this is his cup of tea, in content, in writing style; it leans forward, telling only enough to make the reader want more, and this is the writer's victory.

Returning to the first requirement, note that each lead is persuasive because it is stressing "what's new." True, all four discuss a medical problem. And the "problem" lead is itself a problem; to offer nothing more than a familiar problem is as quick a way as any to kill a lead. But see how each of the four leads connects the cancer problem with its possible solution. That solution, that possibility of a vaccine, is the meat of the story.

A dozen more leads could have been written on the same topic. As we shall see later, the writer could have started with an anecdote, a quotation, a question, an analogy, and so on. Whatever the type or the style, the requirements are the same.

Sometimes good leads come with surprising ease, more often with difficulty. The trouble with the beginner lies less in vocabulary or in sentence structure than in his surrendering too easily and then, in desperation, starting his piece any old way, possibly remembering Francis Bacon's impatience: "Far better it is to make a beginning of that which may lead to something, than to engage in a perpetual struggle and pursuit in courses which have no exit."

But a lead written in defeatism will sound that way. And, of course, the novelist's experimental techniques are not for us. William Faulkner can handle them effectively and has even performed the tour de force of writing the way an idiot thinks. But facts are our business. And they can be troublesome.

This is why. You want to be persuasive, yet disciplined. You have so much to say, and so many statements must be qualified. You keep adding modifiers and explanatory details, and what should be the lead, the display window, becomes the entire department store. The lead has run away with you. If you are a famous writer, or your style is truly suspensive, or your subject is of overpowering importance, you are permitted to bend the requirements. Otherwise you invite trouble if the lead isn't disposed of by the end of the first paragraph or two.

The cure for both novice and professional is much the same. It comes when you suddenly realize that, despite your mass of notes, you have not really digested the material; despite your outline, the pattern isn't clear yet. It's now that the bad lead becomes helpful. It forces you to think out your material, separate wheat from chaff, differentiate main points from details, plan how the different sections will tie together.

Perhaps it wasn't that hard. Perhaps you arrived directly at a realistic outline. In either case, let's assume you are now adequately prepared. What goes into the lead?

FOCUS

You are not writing about everything under the sun, but about a transistor, an experiment, a theory. You presumably have something new to say about it, otherwise why write? Even if you have only researched the literature, then this can be a new bibliography or survey, and, in one way or another, you say so.

Journalists learn this early. Others discover it later, and sometimes the hard way. The thinking in a research report must be as disciplined as in any other writing. "Whenever I am asked by a young and conscientious researcher," says R. E. Speers of Du Pont's Engineering Research Laboratory, "I tell him to start out by trying first to list what he considers his three most significant findings. This usually evokes the question: 'Why only three?' When I tell him that in my limit of three I have already given him a generous margin of two, he is even more bewildered. My point, of course, is that in the majority of research studies there is one principal problem for which a solution is sought."

When more than one subject wants to take lead position, the sensible solution is for you to decide what they have in common. That gets you off to your start. For example, *The Yale Review* asked me to write one review covering two books. The lead:

Turkey is no longer a tinselled Oriental land of harems, and the Turk is no longer unspeakable. Herr Froembgen and Dr. Allen both agree in that. And there the similarity of their books ends. . . .

Or take an article I wrote for *Farm Journal* about a noted horticulturist. The lead would have become hopeless if I had immediately started talking about melons, berries, tomatoes, etc. I found a common denominator, the frost problem in our northern states:

> Many plant breeders *raise* new varieties of fruits and vegetables. But Dr. A. F. Yeager *races* them—races them against the weather.

PUT IT IN FRONT

Focus is not enough if the focal point is not placed solidly in the lead. When we listen to the morning weather broadcast, we want to know quickly whether or not to wear a raincoat—the details about isobars can come later.

It's a fault of scientists the world over to bring the isobars in first. For example, on my desk is a Russian research paper on the "Novikov Gear." That interests me but it is only stubbornness that keeps me reading. Not until after 11 paragraphs discussing the standard involute gear does the author tell me he has something better to offer.

The busy reader is grateful for a true lead; an editor demands it. When discussing a troublesome manuscript with an author, my most frequent question is, "Where's the hero?" By this I mean: Where's the main topic? Both editor and reader want to know quickly. "Did it or didn't it?" "Will it or won't it?" "Can we or can't we?" The answers to these questions belong in the lead. So does the real meat of any other kind. The trimmings, the details, can come later.

If the real meat is neither a question nor an answer, but an "I don't know," then that's your hero and goes in the lead. Thus, after his title "Mars Or Venus?" an Army missiles expert began:

> The primary purpose of this paper, as the title may indicate, is to establish some doubt as to which planet, Mars or Venus, should claim our initial attention. Establishment of doubt may create controversy, controversy spurs research, research results in discoveries—and discovery is sorely needed in this infant space age.

M

THE UNNATURAL PROBLEM

But doesn't bringing the hero to the front seem to demand standing on one's head? Isn't it the problem that comes first? Sometimes it should, as in the detective story with its whodunit answer at the end. But more often, it should not.

The lead that tells the reader nothing new is no lead at all. Such is the lead that merely states a problem he knows very well. It just doesn't make him prick up his ears. What does keep him reading is an answer to a problem. If he's an engineer, for example, he's persuaded to go on reading by leads like these:

> You can have a better cantilever spring by giving it the support of a curved surface. This allows the beam to bend beyond the normal safety limit and thereby overcomes two disadvantages. . . .

> It is no longer necessary to assume that the backlash in a spring clutch is beyond control. Here are two simple ways to . . .

> The problem of choosing swivel joints for a fairly complicated piping system need not be as difficult as it looks at first. . . .

When editing those leads I was reminded of how similar they were, basically, to leads I formerly wrote for instructional articles:

> The ordinary gardener preparing to start seed indoors can easily use a labour-saving trick which some experts have known for several years. . . .

> Here is a good recipe for making those outdoor improvements that you never get round to when the lawn-mowing and gardening season starts. . . .

And from there, the distance is not far to the lead that brings the reader into the laboratory of the problem-solving expert. In a *Reader's Digest* article, I wrote about photogrammetry, the science of aerial mapping:

> From his armchair at Ithaca, New York, Professor Donald Belcher can prospect for oil at Pt. Barrow, Alaska, for water in Iran, or for diamonds in Africa, using nothing but aerial photos.

Or, here, about an ornithologist, for the *Saturday Evening Post*:

Like any man who leads in his field, Dr. Peter Paul Kellogg receives a good many requests for assistance. And since Kellogg's speciality happens to be the highly unusual one . . .

Yes, sometimes the problem itself—without a solution indicated—can be your lead and therefore your story. But it must be fresh in some way. For example, the lead that begins "The unnatural problem of natural gas . . ." fulfils the requirements. It piques the reader's curiosity and indicates content as surely as does "The 7 ways to cure corrosion are . . ." It can be a new problem or it can be an old one with which the reader is hardly acquainted. In an article for *The Yale Review* some years ago, I was explaining the latest aspects of an old problem to readers who knew little about it:

> Alaska has long been a problem child to those who undertake the responsibility of planning for America's future. Not that she has developed into a rebellious adolescent and struck out on her own as colonies sometimes do. She simply has not grown up. . . .

But become familiar with the knack of giving the answer first. This is not hard. It merely takes some practice, and willingness to delay bringing in the problem and other background material.

First, do not be misled by your outline—with its logical breakdown into Problem, Procedure, Discussion, Conclusion; and its further breakdown into "I a", "I b", etc. This is your private table of contents. It can only provide raw material for a lead.

If it's a research report, have a Conclusion at the end if you wish, but first have a true beginning. More and more, such reports now have a Summary—and it comes at the beginning. Furthermore, it's truly a summary. It gives easy highlights—it's the reverse of an Abstract, which repeats the jargon but in a more condensed, therefore more cryptic, form.

The problem can be delayed and so can other background material. There are transition tricks, as you will see in the next chapter, that enable you to name the hero first and then go back to gather up loose ends, state any provisos, give any credits—and then sweep easily back on to to your main trail.

Meanwhile, the direct way is the best. This, from the director of a research group, shows one way of avoiding a cluttered lead:

In the interest of brevity, I deviate from my former lengthy reports and I launch immediately into the record of the developments and accomplishments over the past year.

OTHER GUIDE-LINES

Avoid clutter. Cubs on newspapers and students in journalism school learn the ABC's of their profession by memorizing the five W's required in a lead—Who, Where, What, When, Why—plus an occasional H for How. Other writers can use these reminders too. But they are simply a check-list. They ensure that you won't forget to tell what he won the prize for, or who gave it—or his name. The reporter soon discovers he can write a crisper lead by saving one or two of the W's for later. The following, for example, postpones the Why and How:

> Production of the first synthetic penicillin for medical use, the culmination of a 10-year research programme, was announced last week by the Bristol Laboratories in East Syracuse, New York.

A long lead is better than a short one that doesn't tell enough. But are you sure you cannot write it more crisply? Must so many details be included? Here, the names of the scientists, and how they did it, will come later:

> Soviet scientists have reported discovery of a path into outer space that future space ships will be able to use to escape a dangerous radiation zone.

The overcrisp lead can discourage readers too. Avoid crowding too much into too little space. These contrasting examples are based on the same facts:

Poor: This non-flying primary float-mounted trainer gives students experience in complex helicopter control. Training is step by step, additional functions being added as basic skill develops.

Improved: This captive helicopter can't actually take off. But its powered rotors and complex controls are real. And when mounted on floats, it gives the student a real struggle with troublesome pitching and rolling.

Skilled writers often keep all technical details out of the first paragraph. They depend on suspense to build their lead:

The village swans now swim all winter in the village pond at Laxå, Sweden. Several sawmills are able to use their lumber sluices despite freezing weather. And the Harsfjärden Naval Station can keep its channels open.

These are some experimental applications of a de-icing system . . .

Keep it palatable. When some technical words are needed in the lead, do not let them become jargon. A good rule is this: Whatever you write, however technical, make at least the first few paragraphs understandable to the ordinary reader. For example, this lead from a medical journal can be understood by almost everyone:

Dysphagia means difficult swallowing; the fancy term for painful swallowing is odynophagia. Difficult and painful swallowing may coexist, or either symptom alone may bother the patient. Whether occurring singly or together, however, dysphagia and odynophagia are vitally significant symptoms.

Don't digress. You want the reader to stop and shop. Good writing helps; so does popularization. But no matter how fancy the phrase dancing in your head or how sleek your style, the lead must remain a lead—must get quickly to the point. Here, the analogy is all the more welcome because it departs so soon:

Like the bird that flies backward to see where it has been, America's orbiting "Weather Eye" never looks where it is going. Instead, it keeps its solar-powered camera focused on that section of the earth it has just flown over.

It needn't shout. Many animals have curiosity but man is the only one who reads. Unquestionably, the most effective lead is the type that proclaims something new. And when you find yourself overdoing the word *new*, try variants: *novel, the latest, at last, has now succeeded in,* and the like:

In recent years the efficiency of the axial-flow compressor has reached undreamed-of values. Of the many blade arrangements possible, three—symmetrical, unsymmetrical, and vortex—have become the most popular.

But do everything with moderation. Here's a lead, deadly with problem-problem-problem, which suddenly lapses into breathless advertising copy.

The problem of costly corrosion to ducting systems, resulting from the exhausting of alkali and acid fumes, is a severe problem to thousands of companies.

Comes now a solution to this problem as presented in a new folder by . . .

Like other rules, the "newness" one should be tempered with common sense. Suppose you start a lead this way, "Once upon a time . . ." That sounds childish as well as stale. But it can become a good lead nonetheless:

Once upon a time there was no time as we know it—because there was no cosmos, no starry sky, no light, no speed of light. And of course, without our sun and its spinning, orbiting earth, there were no days and years with which to measure time. Yet the dimension we call time did exist, according to . . .

It labels you. In the lead you reveal some of your own personality. The reader, at least, thinks so. He usually decides quickly whether or not you're his cup of tea. So be very sure your lead is devoid of errors or other embarrassments.

The author whose first words are "This hard-hitting book . . ." may impress the reader as a braggart poaching on the duties of a reviewer. And see how this otherwise interesting lead was spoiled by a dainty dislike of an earthy word:

First comes the prospector, half frontiersman and half scientist. Then the tractor trains chug and creak across frozen lakes and muskegs with essential supplies for a camp. Then come the bush pilots, still flying by their trouser seats. (*But it isn't* trouser seats—*the expression is* "flying by the seat of their pants.")

There is no good reason why a lead should strain for effect and therefore reveal weakness. Nor need it be vulgar to be arresting. When dignity is not merely a disguise for deadliness, it can be powerful. The following, by the late Meyer Berger of the New York *Times*, is a lead admired by newspapermen. Note the stark recital of facts, the power, the restraint:

The first war dead from Europe came home yesterday. The harbor was steeped in Sabbath stillness as they came in on the morning tide in 6,248 coffins in the hold of the transport Joseph V. Connolly.

The Types of Leads

This check-list is not arbitrary. There are no official types of leads. And one version may easily shade into another. But one of the best ways to improve your own leads is to acquaint yourself with the variety available. See which of these samples best approximate your needs.

Textual-functional. This is a matter-of-fact lead that tells what you will be discussing, much as a minister tells what his sermon will be. Three examples:

For a technical manual:
The maintenance procedure for a new type of hot-air furnace is described in this manual. The humidifier here is a non-clog electrical unit that runs on furance current. This does away with the need to replace fouled-up asbestos plates.

For a research report:
A specially processed type of wood has been investigated at our laboratory and found to be almost as effective as lead or graphite for stopping neutrons. . . .

For a research proposal:
We welcome this opportunity to submit a proposal for research on air bearings. The study would carry still further the investigation that we have conducted in the past five years. It would cover the following needs for important additional data. . . .

Textual-literary. Like the functional type, but with more gloss and less appeal to the practical reader. This one, from *Scientific American,* promises well for an article covering the subject "Spider Webs":

When the young spider leaves its silken cocoon, it swings into the world on a silken thread. It weaves a silken net to snare insects, and binds them with silken cords. When danger threatens, the spider drops to safety on silken ropes. . . . When finally a spider dies, it is wrapped (if it has been lucky) in a silken shroud.

Silk is the warp and woof of the spider's life. . . .

Announcement. This can be just the bare "5 W's," but in our field it is improved by supplying some interpretation. The research report mentioned above might result in a commerical announcement like this:

Wood that stops neutrons has been developed by PQ Corporation. This specially processed material, at least twice as effective a shield as ordinary wood, is easier to handle than concrete, and nearly as effective as lead and graphite.

News Pyramid. This type is made possible by the "5 W's" technique. Its advantage is that all of the rest of the story can be abandoned if need be—there is enough in the lead to make sense:

The outbound freighter Mary Doe, caught in heavy fog, crashed into and sank the lightship at Ambrose station early yesterday.

Tabular. Similar to Textual but it spells out your theme very exactly. Three examples of its usefulness:

The need to speed up neutrons for thermonuclear power has led to three new methods . . .

The "space crank" is a new 3-dimensional mechanism that can handle many jobs in the cam and linkage field. It has the simplicity and ruggedness of a 4-bar linkage, but much more versatility. With the space crank you can . . . [five of its strong points are now listed in succession, then the article elaborates on each point].

Nontechnical writers, too, know the value of a tabular lead and some use it very effectively:

There is something sad, and paradoxical, and even a little absurd about the coming election. [After this tabular lead, the next three paragraphs begin: "It is sad because . . ."; "It is paradoxical because . . ."; "And it is absurd because . . ."]

Speech Maker. What a man says can be reported—indirectly —in this way:

World production of synthetic rubber will more than double in the next 10 years, while natural rubber output will remain at about its present levels, a top industry official predicted yesterday.

Direct Quotation. As with the quote that began this chapter, the following example also sets the theme, giving the writer something to comment on:

"No element has gravity or levity within its own element. Every body desires to lose its heaviness."

With these words Leonardo da Vinci expressed something of our intense desire to fly, to lift, to free ourselves. . . .

Reference to Authority. Like the quotation, but allows using the third person:

Charles F. Kettering thought about grass while he was inventing the automobile self-starter. He believed that in chlorophyll, the green coloring matter in grass and leaves, lay the secret of . . .

Interview. This type of lead requires a deft transition (for more on transitions, see the next chapter). From the New York *Times:*

Dr. Hubert A. Lechevalier sat at the end of a long table here today, doodled conic sections on a lined yellow pad, and told what it is like to spend five months working with Russian scientists in their own laboratories.
[transition] The tall, young scientist was speaking from experience still fresh and vivid. He had returned only yesterday . . .

Suspensive. Thor Heyerdahl, the archæologist-explorer, started one of his best-selling books this way:

I had no *aku-aku.*

Nor did I know what an aku-aku was, so I could hardly have used one if I had had it.

Analogy. This is the science writer's best device for explaining the unfamiliar in terms of the familiar:

The latest in atom-smashing cyclotrons is like a merry-go-round. Instead of horses and riders, it whirls atomic particles around, and in ever increasing velocity. When these bullets [analogy again] . . .

Anecdote. Like analogy, it must make a brief entrance, then move out of the way of the main theme:

Sixty years ago when George Washington Carver was seeking new uses for southern crops he discovered 50 new ways by which farmers could cash in on peanuts. But he missed one virtue of the lowly "goober." Last week, ABC Lab. announced that the peanut contains a chemical that can conquer hemophilia, the so-called "bleeder's sickness."

Background. Here are two ways this kind of lead can overcome reader reluctance to dwell in the past:

For a technical manual:

You can become a better helicopter mechanic if you know something of the beginning and early history of this aerial vehicle. Though helicopters didn't come into public notice until after the end of World War II . . .

For a scientific report (from U.S. Navy's Research Reviews):

Ever since the Emperor Penguin was first found incubating its eggs in the antarctic winter at temperatures as low as −77 F, students of animal physiology have wondered how it was possible for the embryos to develop. Until recently, these men could do little more than ponder the question . . .

Statistical. The lead for an annual report can being this way:

In the last 20 years the rate of hospital admissions in this country has greatly increased for almost all diagnostic conditions. Today's hospital patient, however, usually goes home much sooner. These contrasting trends . . .

Alarmist:

"If tonight some global catastrophe wiped out all diagnostic X-ray machines, tomorrow morning the medical profession would find itself back in the 19th century."
The speaker was Professor . . .

Curiosity-rousing:

There is a significant oddity about parts moulded from silicone rubber. Put them to work at challenging high temperatures and they stand up well. But at lower temperatures . . .

Teaser:

How many wives should a husband have—at the same time, that is? This novel topic was the major question discussed by anthropologist Sue Jones . . .

Question-Answer. An effective way to arouse reader interest in a problem he might otherwise consider stale. Two examples:

Getting the most from your research dollars? That depends on your experimental procedure. Too many tests take too much time. Too few don't tell you enough. The method given here allows evaluating all variables. . . .

How far can you design past the yield strength of a structure? The incentive to do so—and still keep this side of collapse—is tempting because here is a region where you begin tapping reserve strength of the material. . . .

New Problem. Here is a lead, freshly phrased, about a problem that is quite new to readers of the engineering journal in which it appeared:

If an engineer were told to design an aircraft for operation on the planet Mars, he would ask for at least two atmosphere values—density and viscosity. An engineer who designs an off-the-road vehicle for a remote part of the world needs similar information. Yet he has never had any measure of the medium in which his vehicle is to operate—no method of soil measurement from a locomotion viewpoint has ever been developed.

Answer to Problem. This, after all, is what most of our readers want:

The first application you think of for the integrated system described here is monitoring the movement of aircraft in a congested area. You see not only the present locations of the planes but their flight patterns.

Research Summary. Readers of research reports bless the writers who use this increasingly popular device. It comes ahead of the report and tells what it's about. This means it is a lead, in a sense. How nicely it can mesh with a workmanlike lead is shown in this technical paper published by *Analytical Chemistry:*

Summary: An attempt was made to resolve a mixture of close-boiling nitriles by gas chromatography. Single columns different in nature and length were tried without much success. During the experimental part of this work, it was observed that the order of elution of nitriles on a nonpolar column is different from that on a polar one, and this phenomenon formed a basis for the technique described.

Lead: The method utilizes two modes of gas chromatographic separations. One is based on . . . The other is based on . . .

Memo. Here, certainly, you should appeal directly to the busy reader, and go straight to the point:

From two years of research and prototype development we are [I am] convinced that our company should immediately set up . . .

12

PUTTING THE PIECES TOGETHER

AFTER the lead, what? How do you take command of the details that all seem to be wanting to speak at once?

For a satisfactory lead, you had to tie your facts and thoughts into neat bundles. Maybe you drew from a written outline, backed by file cards; possibly from a pattern carried in your head; perhaps even, from an array of envelopes into which you had tucked like-minded paragraphs.

Your paper could now go ahead and write itself—except for one thing. It cannot write itself. Besides facts and thoughts, the reader needs transitions, needs them as surely as he needs punctuation.

Within a badly constructed paragraph he can often jump from one sentence to the next, supplying his own relevancy. But between paragraphs he needs the trustworthy little foot-bridges called transitions. Without them he quickly demands, "What's the connection?"—just as an editor sighs, "It doesn't track."

In a tabular lead, for example, you inform the reader that you will be discussing several points, But how, after the lead, do you let the reader know he is passing from one point to the next? The simplest way, of course, is to list them: a, b, c, or 1, 2, 3. But that can be oppressive. And you can tell much more with words. So you start each paragraph with a transition device of its own: "Most important is the . . ."; "Another way to accomplish . . ."; "The most popular method . . ."; "Some chemists even try . . ."

Or suppose your lead gives an answer. How do you now backtrack to the problem, and then turn back again to the chronological sequence that solved it?

And always there are the nagging details: Where do you find places for those background facts that couldn't crowd into the lead but must be given quickly? How can you interrupt the flow, to bring in whatever disclaimers you may have to make?

As with leads, the devices of transition do not lend themselves to rigid rule-making, and the subject is usually passed over quickly if it is mentioned at all. And as with leads, transitions can best be taught by examples. The trick no longer seems formidable when you see how easily it can be done by turning a sentence round into a question, or by merely inserting "But." I have found that students become adept quickly—once they understand the necessity of placing a bridge between the lead and body of the paper, and linking the paragraphs that follow.

Here, for example, the writer is past his lead. He now fails to tie the next two paragraphs together properly; the reader stumbles at "Today":

> The warning that there will be fewer physicians and dentists just when people need more medical and dental care came from a consultant committee to the Surgeon General of the United States.
> Today, as a result of a number of factors, our people are demanding more medical and dental care than ever before. One of these factors is health and hospital insurance. . . .

The second paragraph can be improved several ways; most important, with a transition:

> *The committee explained* that a combination of factors underlies today's growing demand for such care. One of these is health and hospital insurance. . . .

Here is another example of a bad transition after the lead:

Such sciences as chemistry and physics are exact and specific in their elementary stages. For example, the boiling point of water is definitely known to be 100 deg C, and the formula for sulphuric acid is unquestionably H_2SO_4.

Freshmen in chemistry find little difficulty in distinguishing between homogeneous and heterogeneous dispersions. . . .

After the first dozen words of the second paragraph, I have to go back to the first paragraph and hunt for a connection. Why not supply it to the reader with a second paragraph like this?

This precision helps the beginner. The chemistry freshman, for instance, quickly learns how to distinguish between homogeneous and heterogeneous dispersions. . . .

When absence of transition is joined by presence of jargon, the reader must indeed pause and ponder. Let's return to the leads in Chapter 11 (page 165) that deal with a cancer vaccine. Suppose I wrote this lead:

Research is being carried out by several organizations to produce an effective defence system against cancer. What they are seeking is a vaccine.

Among the RES boosters, B.C.G. is believed to be the most vigorous. When it was injected into mice, it produced complete recovery. . . .

The first paragraph will do. But what connection does it have with the next (and with the alien words dropped upon us so abruptly)?

The cure isn't difficult. Discard that second paragraph and substitute two others, each with a transition:

Its job would be to stimulate the antibody-producing activities of the RES. This network of cellular tissue found in the spleen, liver, bone marrow and lymph nodes guards us against harmful bacteria and other invaders.

We already have *such boosters*. Among them, B.C.G. (Bacillus Calmette Guerin) is believed to be the most vigorous. . . .

Those transitions are at the beginning of the paper. The same method applies throughout. Transitions breathe life into the outline. Here the same subject is discussed in the form of a report summarizing research activities. Note the professional skill with which the writer, a student, brings in transitions that carry the reader from point to point of the outline. The successive paragraphs begin with the following sentences or phrases:

> The year just concluded marks a turning point . . .
> Until now, cancer therapy has seemed irrevocably restricted . . .
> Today it appears that by utilizing the incomparable defences . . .
> Massive research projects of varied nature made this possible . . .
> 1. Research into the nature of the body's defence system . . .
> 2. Artificial cultivation of antibodies . . .
> 3. Research to develop a vaccine that will stimulate . . .
> The element common to these researches . . .
> Investigations now being carried on independently at . . .
> New York University reports . . .
> M.I.T. announces that it is on the trail . . .
> And lastly, the University of Virginia reports . . .
> The second major line of research is . . .
> Creative as they are, these researches . . .
> B.C.G. (Bacillus Calmette Guerin) is the most vigorous of these . . .
> Experimental immunization of animals has also shown . . .
> This discovery . . .
> The experiments were designed to test . . .
> Extreme contrast marked the reaction of the two groups . . .
> Following the second implantation, however . . .
> These experiments demonstrate two striking facts . . .
> In cancer, the defensive system is broken down by . . .
> What are the implications of these researches?
> Whatever the results, one thing is certain . . .

CONQUERING THE BACKGROUND

To see more precisely how transitions are created and manipulated, let's first examine the place in your paper where, unless you write straight narrative, a suitable transition is most necessary—and most troublesome.

This comes just ahead of the body of your presentation. This short section that follows the lead might be part of a paragraph; it might run to two paragraphs. It has to be ushered in by a transition and then it must be followed by another transition, the one that puts the reader back on the track.

Why this fuss? Because between the lead and the rest you almost always have to set the stage, or do some tidying, or make some excuses, or define some terms, or insert some background. Here you must take time to explain that the abbreviation RES is the body's defence network. Here you state that your report is the fifth in a series, or was done under such-and-such auspices. Here, if your lead offers an answer, you protect yourself with qualifications or by indicating the nature of your evidence. In the following, the proofs were announced twice: midway in the two-paragraph lead, and again in the next paragraph.

> Have you noticed how much more talk there is about milk fever and ketosis these days? And how the list of new treatments keeps growing?
>
> *Even veterinarians admit* it's all pretty complex and hard to keep up with. But maybe we've been innocently bringing these costly and mysterious troubles on ourselves—just by wrong feeding.
>
> *That's the belief of several top-notch dairymen*, who are now having less trouble with these diseases . . .

When you have to insert some background, this can be done deftly. For example, in a *Popular Science Monthly* article called "Lindbergh's Amazing Airplane," the lead correctly dealt with what was new—it was the thirtieth anniversary of Lindbergh's solo flight across the Atlantic. Then came a qualifier and some background:

> Actually, the plane almost didn't get off the ground at all. Lindbergh had been rebuffed, in his search for a plane, by Bellanca, Fokker, Travel Air and Columbia. Bellanca insisted that no single-engine plane could fly the Atlantic.

And now the body—back to the main track of this article:

> But on Feb. 23, 1927, Lindbergh walked into the office of Ryan Airlines on Juniper St., San Diego ,Calif., and within hours signed a contract. . . .

Even if the background material takes much more than that one paragraph, it can be treated the same way. In Smyth's book

Atomic Energy for Military Purposes (published in 1945), the secondary material was both fresh and necessary because so much of it had been kept secret. He therefore began his book with it and went on chronologically. But when Michael Amrine wrote his history *The Great Decision* (published in 1959), he was revealing political secrets of the A-bomb. Its technical details were now less important. He consequently began with the death of Franklin D. Roosevelt:

> At five o'clock this spring afternoon the Vice-President was running—alone—through the basement of the Capitol.

Amrine saved his second chapter for background material about the bomb and then, with the reader satisfied, went on with the narrative.

Now what about that major nuisance, the technical problem (see page 170)? We want the lead to be persuasively fresh, to offer a "hero" who solves the problem. We don't want the lead to be nothing more than the statement of a problem the reader already knows. Here is how a technical article reached the rewrite desk:

> Conventional cantilever springs do not make efficient use of available space unless they are modified in some fashion, as are the triangular, trapezoidal, parabolic or tapered-beam springs discussed in Dr. —— ——'s recent article. . . . The reason for the inefficiency is that . . . There is another drawback. . . . These disadvantages—volume inefficiency and tendency to overstress—can be avoided by curving the support of the spring, Fig. 1. Under load a conventional cantilever spring assumes a parabolic shape. The radius of curvature . . . the spring begins to roll over the curved support.

That version started off negatively, was loaded with dull background and required the reader to reel through 193 words before he had enough clues to guess the writer's meaning.

Note how different is the rewritten version. Instead of the wordy problem, the "hero" comes first and speaks with self-assurance:

> You can have a better cantilever spring by giving it the support of a curved surface. This allows the beam to bend beyond the

normal safety limit and thereby overcomes the two disadvantages that otherwise limit performance of the cantilever:

1. It prevents overstress. Excessive deflection—from a sudden shock load, or overtravel of a lever—no longer can break the spring or give it a permanent set.

2. It increases energy that can safely be stored in the spring. By itself, a cantilever does not make best use of materials, because all sections are not sharing the work equally.

What happened here? The true lead—the answer—now comes first. It leans forward in the sense of making the reader want to know more. But it also disposes of the background by means of a neat trick: It defines the advantages as being a lack of the disadvantages. Details can follow. Meanwhile, the reader is told more, and in less than half as many words.

In that example the transitions are clear-cut. The first paragraph ends with a colon and the next two refer right back to the new method with a number and an "It."

The transition becomes slightly more worrisome when the lead is followed by a qualifier or disclaimer of some sort. But here, too, the procedure need not be complicated. A news dispatch says:

Space engineers agreed today that flying laboratories should be circling the earth soon.

Although they differed on ways of putting space stations into orbit, the engineers saw certain requirements as basic to the first manned projects:

The first transition, *Although*, introduces the brief qualifier. And the next transition, the colon, will bring the reader back into the development of this story.

One of the handiest uses for the short section between lead and body is as a carrier for a needed qualifier. Its position in front gives a scientist his chance to hedge on everything that follows. For example, the chairman of a geography department builds an article around the quoted statement that orbiting television systems are "the most revolutionary step forward in understanding and predicting the weather."

Then the disarming transition:

This bold claim may take some living up to, but no one doubts that Tiros is a step in the right direction. . . .

Or, here a rather weak alibi tries to save a rather weak research report:

> The widely accepted idea that the emotional character of individuals depends greatly on early relationship with the mother has been confirmed by research at the American Musuem of Natural History.
> The museum's study *is not a project for the verification of truisms,* but a part of a long-range research program. . . .

But here, in a skilful succession of lead, background and qualification, the writer took weakness and converted it to strength:

> A tiny probe invented by two M.I.T. metallurgists may reveal that certain priceless masterpieces owned by the world's leading museums and collectors are worthless except as curiosities.
> In its first test, at the Boston Museum of Fine Arts, the needle exposed a 15th century portrait as a fraud and proved that it dated from the era of flappers and bootleg gin instead of the age of Botticelli and da Vinci.
> *In a sense the test was rigged.* The museum had already discovered that the painting was not genuine, but the object of the trial was to determine whether the needle could detect and verify the forgery. It did both.

Another example. In the preceding chapter (page 175), you read the lead of an article from *Scientific American* on spiders. Now see how that paragraph was followed by this one that bundles up and disposes of any quibbles, while it continues with background needed for the body of the article:

> Silk is the warp and woof of the spider's life. *A few other* creatures secrete silk, *but none* has exploited its possibilities so fully. With their unique mastery of this technology, spiders have colonized the entire habitable world and evolved some 40,000 species. *Not all* of them spin their silk into webs. The wolf spider, for example, chases its quarry, the jumping spider stalks it, and the crab spider hides and pounces. *But most* spiders do spin webs, and the success of the spider is only one aspect of the success of the web.

Occasionally the disclaimer can be disposed of right in the lead—if done in few words and without too much qualifying. This is from a business paper for engineers:

> Although they cannot compete with zinc for purely decorative forms, aluminium diecastings fulfil many mechanical requirements for structural components. And two new developments—a new alloy and a refinement of the vacuum die-casting process—promise to give them even wider usefulness.

If the qualifier, background, or other interruptive material does come right after the lead, how do you then get back on the track? It's as easy as it was getting off the track: with a transition word or phrase. Here's a new-product announcement:

> We have developed a new plastic flooring material. Called ——, it is used to resurface and patch concrete floors.
> *Formerly* it was necessary to replace the floor completely or to cover the worn area with a metal plate. Both these methods are expensive and inefficient.
> *Now, as shown by extensive tests,* there is no longer need for metal plates, and thousands of dollars can be saved in maintenance costs. The new material contains . . .

And here is a story from a science news service:

> —An electric tractor that can tug a multiple-bottom plough through parched, packed earth with a pull of 3,000 pounds has been created here.
> *Although* the tractor is strictly experimental, it points to the start of a revolution in powered farm machinery—a revolution that could spill over into the automotive field.
> *Instead of having an ordinary engine,* the tractor houses a small army of 1,008 fuel cells under its hood . . .

THE FLOW PATTERN

The procedure in developing your paper, through the lead and thereafter, becomes something more than the routine of following an outline from Problem to Conclusion. The outline must now become a guide that shows you what to tell the reader at the different stages.

True, organizing the material in this functional fashion is not smooth going. That is why everybody on a magazine, for example, likes to write the editorial. To the amateur, it seems so easy. No need to marshal facts—and to find them first. Just let your prejudices spin out in your most resplendent prose. That is why so many editorials are empty.

The flow of information must go through steps that are quite well defined even though they allow for variations. They could be shown in chart form, but it's just as easy to describe the logical sequence.

The reader's first meeting with your offering is ordinarily in the headline or title of the piece. It may be phrased in one of several ways. It could be an alliterative play on words, it could be a teasing paradox, it could be solidly sober. In any case, like the lead later on, it should attract the busy reader with a promise to discuss something interesting. And, of course, it must be very much condensed. Always, the actual wording should depend on the interests of the particular audience you want to attract. For example:

    Pneumatics Simulates Electronics
    Effect of Tranquilizers on the Brain
    Man-made Material Is Hard as Diamond
    How to Design with Swivel Joints
    Has Science Lost Its Courage?
    Tight Tolerances Can Be Even Tighter
    Solution by Analogy
    Tiny Submarine Manœuvres like a Plane
    Physiological Approach to Space Problems
    You Can Whip the Backlash in Spring Clutches

Next, if the piece is an article in a magazine or house organ, or a report in a newspaper, the reader is given something more to whet his appetite. It's done with what the newspaper headline writer calls his "deck" or "bank." Some magazines use the same name for it; others call it the subtitle; business papers frequently call it the "blurb." In magazines, it's the editor talking—hawking his wares, if you will.

For example, the second of the two leads on page 163 might have come from a sober article titled "The Crystals Called Whiskers." And the deck might read:

Besides learning how and why these hairlike crystals grow, science has found in many of them a strength far surpassing that of the leading superalloys. Will these powerful filaments, already a valuable tool for the researcher, eventually revolutionize the technology of structural materials?

The reader is now farther along. The entire article has been summarized, though quite sketchily. The trick was to say it briefly in the title; then, with a transition, to tell more in the deck. The transition was " . . . these hairlike crystals . . ."—it refers directly back to the title.

Next, of course, comes the lead. Here you cannot assume more than that the reader has been persuaded to stop at your piece and give it a try. He now wants the entire story in orderly fashion—and from you, not from the title and deck. You therefore start afresh with the highlights, follow with any detour you may need, and then resume the main theme in logical sequences. It is in the later stages that your original outline can come in handy as a guide, but only with transitions that carry the reader over one footbridge after another. As the information flows, from paragraph to paragraph, you anticipate the transitions. It's like remembering to insert the steel bars that join successive pourings of reinforced concrete; in music, it's like working into a modulation, where a chord common to both keys is used as the pivot.

For example, in an article called "Weapons Secret and Scientific," I had the problem of explaining radar to readers of *The Antioch Review*. They were not all scientists and, moreover, had heard little about this hush-hush subject. World War II had just ended.

The lead therefore was general. It began, "Far larger than the B-29, secrecy spanned the entire global war. Its wings rested protectively over each D-Day . . . ." It ended on the theme "But secrecy is automatically faced by its opposite number, espionage. . . ."

The next paragraph began with an unmistakable transition: "It was so with radar. . . . This was the art of sending radio pulses . . ." (and readers were given a quick explanation in general terms—the technical details could come later).

A second transition was now sufficient to send the reader on his way into the article: "Originally, it was a detection device. But when this marvellous eye was synchronized with . . ."

How easily the later transitions can be supplied when the lead-off portion has been handled well is seen in a *Fortune* article, "Great American Scientists: The Chemists." One sequence of paragraphs has these beginnings:

> Up to 1920, America had taken only one Nobel Prize . . .
> The year 1920, therefore, may stand as a significant starting point . . .
> The year 1920 has other useful distinctions . . .

Another sequence concerns big molecules:

> The leading architect in molecular construction is 43-year-old Robert Burns Woodward . . .
> Woodward's first major feat was to complete . . .
> It would be a mistake to think that all problems in synthesis . . .

The last example shows that it is not vitally important just where in the transition sentence the transition word or phrase occurs. That sentence might have read: "All problems in synthesis, however, are not . . ."

The main requirements are clarity and effectiveness. Remembering them is more important than trying to follow a pedagogical rule that orders you to place the "most striking" words at the beginning of a sentence. How the previous paragraph ends will dictate how the next should begin, whether the next should be one of these two:

> Frank Lloyd Wright was such a giant in architecture.
> Such a giant in architecture was Frank Lloyd Wright.

In other words, if composing a good lead helps you clarify your thoughts, it is equally true that providing good transitions keeps your thoughts from wandering. Your exposition stays in context, and the reader is grateful.

Transition Devices

The choice depends on agility of the writer. There is no handbook of transitions. However, there is an assortment of types that can serve as models.

1. Among the simplest are the ordinary linking words. There are so many that we have little excuse for using any of them over and over until they become shopworn. The links include such words as *also, however, likewise, moreover, now, thus, then, next.* Here again, context is more important than position in the sentence. Either of these would do, depending on what went before:

> Thermonuclear power is the next step.
> The next step is thermonuclear power.

2. Phrases are also helpful—and doubly so when they are brought in as resting spots for the reader ploughing through heavy technical material; for example, when a scientist begins his next paragraph with "Let us now examine . . ." or "Suppose that . . ." But practice moderation. The method easily becomes boring if carried to excess. Here a writer overdid it, with rest-phrase transitions starting each of five succeeding paragraphs:

> This led some of us to conclude that . . .
> It is well to emphasize that . . .
> It is known that if one takes . . .
> It is precisely this general type . . .
> In other words . . .

Why not vary the phrase method with others, as I do in the following sequence of four paragraph-beginnings?

> The introductory phrase leans forward and backward. It refers to what we have been talking about, and what we are now talking about.
>
> *In other words*, it's a transition device . . .
> The best of *these* . . .
> Linkage words are *another way* . . .

3. Influence words (Chapter 7, page 111) can provide transitions too. They do this while accenting the meaning:

> *Equally* important is temperature . . .
> That is not the *only* method . . .

Among them is the powerful qualifier *but*:

> *But* Alcoa claims this initial cost difference . . .
> *But if* you visualize the electron as a . . .

4. Turning a declarative sentence into a question is one of the easiest transition devices known to editors, and I have found that students pick up this technique quickly. First, a pair of paragraphs that need transition:

> Ablation is a surgical term adapted by rocket men. It means gradual erosion of the surface of a body while underlying material remains essentially unaffected. This is why some meteors survive when they enter the earth's atmosphere.
> It is believed possible to design materials that will enable space vehicles to re-enter the atmosphere without being consumed by the heat of friction.

Now let's begin that second paragraph with a question:

> Can man design materials that will protect themselves in the same way? They would enable space vehicles to re-enter the atmosphere without being consumed by the heat of friction. This is indeed possible . . .

Similarly, a weak transition can be changed to a stronger one:

> The cause of the infection can be traced to . . .
> What is the cause of this infection? It can be traced to . . .

5. The echo method—repeating a key word—is quite all right if it is not employed in exactly the same way each time and if the repetition also serves some other purpose. In the medical article about dysphagia (Chapter 11, page 173), the transition word was usually dysphagia itself. This was justifiable because the word has no ready synonyms; also because the paragraphs were long ones and the reader therefore had no feeling that dysphagia was being drummed at him. This is the way each of five succeeding paragraphs began:

> If advantage is to be taken of the high degree of reliability of *dysphagia* as a symptom, it must be . . .
> On the positive side, two types of *dysphagia* can usually . . .
> When a patient has esophageal *dysphagia* . . .
> When *dysphagia* is caused by disease at the . . .
> Next to *dysphagia*, pain is the most important symptom . . .

6. A more common way to use the echo, of course, is with synonyms. This method serves double duty because it is also the paraphrasing way of getting around jargon (Chapter 5, page 78). Here a newspaperman used transition to tie two paragraphs together while explaining the new word:

> Ocean depths never before explored have been reached by the bathyscaphe Trieste, the Naval Electronics Laboratory announced today.
> The cigar-shaped, 75-ton vessel descended four and a half miles beneath the surface of the ocean . . ..

7. Perhaps the easiest of all transitional devices is the simple word *this*. In the foregoing example, as the second paragraph stepped forward it was guided by an echo signal from the first paragraph. That is, it referred right back to *bathyscaphe*. But the echoing could have been done in the opposite way. Here, I switch positions of *bathyscaphe* and the words describing it:

> Ocean depths never before explored have been reached by a cigar-shaped, 75 ton vessel, the Naval Electronics Laboratory announced today.
> This craft, called a bathyscaphe, descended four . . .

And, of course, it could also have been:

> The craft, called a bathyscaphe, descended four . . .

Usually *this* is superior to *the* as a transition word because it is more specific. For example, here is a short lead, followed by alternative ways to begin the next paragraph:

> "Outstanding" was the performance rating given the nations' largest operating nuclear power reactor.
> The first full-scale, privately financed nuclear power station in the world, it is situated near . . .
> This first full-scale, privately financed nuclear power station in the world is situated near . . .

8. In general, the transition should be more than a convenience. It can even become the most important part of the paragraph, as in this feature story from the New York *World-Telegram and Sun*:

The politico-entomological world rippled with wonder, dismay and faint laughter today as word got around about Dr. Charles Garrett and his "muggle bug."

What in heaven's name is a muggle bug? people asked. . . .

13

THE SECOND LOOK

I WOULD like to have called this chapter "The Morning After," but that might have connotations of bleariness. I am recommending the exact opposite—a coolly fresh pair of eyes. Whose eyes? Yours. Why should they be fresh? Because yesterday, or the week before perhaps, you assembled your first draft. As Robert Louis Stevenson explained it in a letter to a friend, you macerated your subject, then let it boil slow, and now is the time to "take the lid off and look in. There your stuff is, good or bad."

It is now that you examine the concoction with an alert, critical, even skeptical look. In the cold glare of a new day it's probably not as good as it seemed. It may even sound like awful drivel. But that's being harsh. If you really worked conscientiously on the first draft, if you burned your candle at both its ends, the manuscript is not that bad. But "ah, my foes," and "oh, my friends," it certainly can stand various ministrations: laundering, pruning, polishing.

And those are your responsibilities. For whatever else you call yourself—proposal writer, student, scientist, journalist—you are the first editor who will see what you wrote. And your editing is required, even if it's nothing more than checking the letter you dictated, to confirm that you ended it with "Yours Truly."

It is this self-editing, this scanning that leads to a second draft and perhaps more drafts, that decides the success of your message. This is no time to be easily satisfied, to nod in agreement with yourself, or to doze off under the droning spell of your prose. Montaigne put it this way:

> Arts and sciences are not cast in a mould, but are formed and perfected by degrees, by often handling and polishing, as bears leisurely lick their cubs into form.

But how much handling and what kind of polishing when we practice the art of science writing? One of the purposes of this chapter is to provide a check-list—telling specifically where to look for trouble makers. This guide is at the end of the chapter.

The same list can, of course, be a useful guide when we are in the first throes of composition. But our hands are full then with such over-all problems as deciding on the lead and organizing the rest clearly and effectively. This is why the professional sets a fairly loose set of standards for the first draft; he relies on the second look and its tighter standards to weed out the verbiage, decide the fine points of punctuation and spelling, catch embarrassing words and phrases, sharpen points, brighten passages—and perhaps even perform major surgery. If, like a journalist, he doesn't consult an actual check-list, this is because he carries it in his head.

One of the surest signs that a beginner will remain a beginner is his assumption that his writing is so good that it does not need changes. The craftsman usually makes an assumption too: He will probably have to do at least one more version. It would be hard to believe that writing such as this by Donald Culross Peattie underwent no changes:

> The beauty of a butterfly's wing, the beauty of all things, is not a slave to purpose, a drudge sold to futurity. It is excrescence, superabundance, random ebullience, and sheer delightful waste to be enjoyed in its own right.

That, of course, is the appreciator's type of prose suitable to a naturalist. Writers about merchandise aren't so lavish. But the same polishing and distilling, the same striving for the *mot juste* is found in the following sinewy writing—almost a shorthand but with impeccable hyphenation and therefore always comprehensible—which serves as the caption for a photograph in the "New Products" section of *Progressive Architecture* magazine:

> . . . combines illumination with low-velocity air diffusion in same fixture. Unit consists of glass-bottom, flush-mounted, fluorescent-lighting fixture with tiny side-slots which transmit vertical air flow from low-velocity diffuser attached above. Diffuser is connected by flexible tube to central duct in drop ceiling. Lighting fixture is the only part visible below.

Both examples show the same writing care that is found in important documents. In *The Great Decision*, Michael Amrine relates:

> All during this week, staff members worked far into the night, making drafts of memos and communiqués and working on the main military document to be prepared—an item that became known to history as the Potsdam Declaration. From time to time a page or a paragraph would be brought to the higher-ups and then taken back to the workshops to be polished or perhaps completely revised. . . .

To see more closely how it's done, let's visit the Berg Collection at the main branch of New York City's public library and examine some original manuscripts. For example, we note the four successive versions of the opening sentence of John Gunther's book *Death Be Not Proud*, which tells the story of his son, who died at 17. I italicize the changes that show how the sentence was revised to come nearer what the author wanted to say:

> This is not so much a memoir of Johnny but the story of a long struggle between a child and Death.

> This is not so much a memoir of Johnny *as it is* the story of a long struggle between a child and Death.

> This is not so much a memoir *in the ordinary sense as* the story of a long *courageous* struggle between a child and Death.

> This is not so much a memoir *of Johnny* in the *conventional* sense as the story of a long *invincible* struggle between a child and Death.

If the professional writer takes that much care, if Beethoven wrote four overtures for *Fidelio* and tried more than two hundred ideas for the triumphant chorale in his Ninth Symphony, it is surely presumptuous for a fledgling writer to think his first draft is final—or needs only a proofreader's glance.

And if he does hear the call for editing but simply passes the chore on to an editor, then his becomes the unpopularity of anybody who has been expected to wash his personal linen, but didn't. Unless, that is, he can write a thank-you note like this: "You did a terrific job in 'translating' my original manuscript into an article of which I am proud to be author."

It is another sign of the amateur, however, that he too often cries anguish when an editor makes the necessary changes. True, this sometimes alters the meaning he intended, but he can blame only his ambiguities and himself. Science writing has not yet reached the stage where a large-enough corps of appropriately specialized editors is available to handle it. Too many editors get lost in this jargon. Technical books, for example, are classic illustrations of bad writing that receives only minor editing; the rest, the reader must do for himself. There are some signs of change forced by the need for better communication. Science-minded editors have begun manning copy desks. Various magazines in the field are proclaiming such innovations as "Distilled Writing" and "Creative Editing." Even a professional rewrite service has made its début. Nevertheless, the initial responsibility remains with the author—he presumably knows his subject best.

The professional writer, too, may not always be eager to wash his own linen. But he knows that doing so lessens the chance that a harassed editor will accidentally change the meaning while rewriting a sentence or paragraph, or substitute "altitude of the aeroplane" when the writer really meant "attitude of the aeroplane." The pro knows something else that would turn many people into happier and better writers. He has learned that, with practice, surgery on one's own writing becomes less painful. Each cut isn't to the quick, or to the soul; rather, it's the pruning that produces a better tree.

Furthermore, knowing that a second look is coming, he needn't feel so desperate when he's doing the first draft. He overcomes the psychological barrier that stops many would-be writers. He simply says, "I can do it. And now I'll start. It needn't be perfect just yet."

This is why he likely writes rapidly first, as fast as his words roll out, knowing he can trim away any fat later. Or, if his subject is complicated, he may do the draft rather sketchily, satisfied if he has a workmanlike lead and if other pieces fall into place reasonably well—though they may be held together at this stage with nothing more permanent than bubble gum and safety pins; in other words, with imperfect transitions and with the possibility that a paragraph or section may later have to be transposed. But that will be only labour, not the frenzy of composition.

Aside from this less worried approach, self-editing is much the same for pro or beginner. Its depth depends mostly on circumstances. If you are extraordinary or your assignment is extraordinarily easy, the draft may need only the simplest polishing—for typographical errors and such. More likely, it will need a copy-editing job—to weed out verbiage, sharpen meanings, catch inelegancies. And often the quickest way is a complete rewrite.

A "Help Wanted" advertisement for an expensive copy editor gives the specifications as follows:

1. Intelligent (penetrates at once to core of the matter)
2. Well educated (preferably liberal arts)
3. A perfectionist in syntax (conversant with Strunk, Fowler, etc.)

Self-editing can be on a less expert level but the approach is similar. It plugs holes in continuity, sharpens words, tears out weeds, sews with good transition thread what was held together with pins, changes sequence where necessary, and so on. It's like the bear licking her cub, like a sculptor chipping away to get the structure of features but retain attractive roundness too. In all this we need be no different from the good fiction writer. Listen to Rudyard Kipling, who became a vivid writer of prose by ruthless and repeated self-editing:

A tale from which pieces have been raked out is like a fire that has been poked—it burns hot and bright because the air can blow through.

o

VERBIAGE

This is the bulkiest problem. Ideally, the first draft should be written a bit lean. That would allow the luxury of fattening it later with a bright analogy here, an apt quotation there. In actuality, most of us overwrite because so much is demanding to be said. This gives the superfluity that must come out later—especially if only so many words or pages have been allotted to the piece.

The skilled writer prefers one way, the beginner another. The former looks for entire paragraphs and sections that can be eliminated. This is the fastest method. It avoids slicing sentences and trimming phrases to the point where they turn cryptic. And if you are far beyond a prescribed word limit, this method hurts less than the painful snipping and deleting of tiny pieces—a torture reminiscent of old China's "death by a thousand slices."

The beginner is apt not to realize this. The very thought of scuttling some of those well-written paragraphs is horrifying. He also fears that he will be condemned for omissions that would indicate he doesn't know his subject thoroughly. But here his trouble is not so much one of verbiage as of faulty judgment, of feeling that every subtheme must be laboriously developed to its end. He falls into the error that led Macaulay to review a biography of Lord Burleigh in this derisive way:

> The title is as long as an ordinary preface; the prefatory matter would furnish out an ordinary book; and the book contains as much reading as an ordinary library . . . it consists of about two thousand closely printed quarto pages, occupies fifteen hundred inches cubic measure, and weighs sixty pounds avoirdupois. . . .

Taking big bites out of your manuscript is quite simple. For instance, you may be discussing the proper feeding of milch cows. Their nutritional problems during pregnancy are interestingly similar to those of the human mother before her baby is born. But you do not have enough space to explore that side avenue. Your article is about feeding during the cow's months of lactation. So you wipe out the need for five or ten paragraphs with a once-over-lightly phrase:

In addition to the special problems faced just before birth of her calf, the cow must be prepared for the heavy drain that a long milking period will place on her reserves. This drain begins . . .

Or, in a report analyzing the mistakes found in science writing, you sacrifice several nonessential paragraphs:

Whatever the causes of the scientist's troubles with language, clarity is the ultimate victim. There are the cryptic passages, the errors in grammar, the ambiguities. . . .

At other times, the method of removing slices is adequate, and not over painful. For example, a paragraph may be overblown with billowing sentences. Good writing does allow room for "rest phrases," as we have said, especially when they help the reader through a paragraph composed of long sentences that are technical in content. But in the following passage (with my italics), from an architectural journal, the sentences are not overlong and not technical, yet they are so fat that, like Falstaff, they lard the lean earth as they walk:

There is one other item *I would like to mention briefly in respect to* the neighbourhood. Neighbourhoods are created from the raw product of land. *What we find is that* land is being developed as a site for dwellings connected by streets and utilities. *In so doing,* the landscape is changed, very seldom for the better, usually for the worse.

If you don't have the courage to throw out that rather meaningless paragraph, at least cut it to:

Something else about neighbourhoods: They are merely dwellings connected by streets and utilities. As the sites are developed, the landscape changes, usually for the worse.

To prune a sentence you must, of course, focus on the words within it. Sociologists have been accused of including three invented words, three misused words, and three superfluous words in every ten words they write. That is an exaggeration, but it points to a weakness found in many "ologies," physical as well as social.

So you look for many things. Perhaps it's simply a fondness for the word *the.* "Where *the* beauty of *the* design and *the* honesty of *the* structure . . ." becomes shorter and also more effective when cut to "where beauty of design and honesty of structure. . . ." Perhaps it's a fondness for prepositions. "Each of the transistors" can be compressed to "each transistor" or "both transistors." When you spot a redundancy like "prototype model," choose one word or the other. And while at it, you might see value in using the word *prototypical*.

You also seek passages that protest too much—qualifications and further details piled on each other, as in the language of law, which has been described as "sacrificing brevity to make sure of clarity and too often losing both." It is no accident that a newspaperman sometimes writes his best story under pressure—he hasn't time to bog down in extras.

And when you are simplifying jargon, ask yourself if even the simplified version is anything more than an unneeded embellishment of the obvious. Equations are often necessary. But what of nonsense such as this?

Let Cost of Production be a, Sales be b, and Profit be c.
Then $b - a = c$.

THE BIGGEST EMBARRASSMENT

Eliminating verbosity is not the only point covered in the checklist. Certainly the quality of the words—not just the quantity—is also important. This is why we prefer concrete nouns and verbs that do things. It is also why we watch out for trouble makers— the careless "influence word" that might throw you into a libel suit; the words in a business proposal that are noisily aggressive rather than self-confident; the "weasel" words and words of bad taste; the would-be clever words; and, yes, the words that don't tell the facts.

But of all embarrassments, the most common is the misspelled word.

Bad spelling is the fault a reader notices before all else. It is not enough to envy "good writers." Some of them, too, spell badly. Nor, in our field, is it enough to blame the difficult words of science. In the same morning, manuscripts come to my desk with such words as *homogenous*, admittedly sly when it trespasses on *homo-*

geneous, and more blatant wrongdoers: *inexcessable, flour carbon* (for *fluorocarbon*), *tarrif,* and the like.

Those embarrassments didn't get into print. But even if an editor or proofreader fields your errors, you have already damaged yourself by the very act of writing such words as *sattelite* and *aperature.* They bespeak sloppiness, and your facts become suspect too.

This may seem a high price to pay for not having consulted the dictionary. But it happens to be the price, especially in science, where writing should instil confidence.

I am not speaking here of typographical errors or other accidents—the mortifying kind that changes *ballet dancer* to *belly dancer* and *comely girl* to *homely girl.* Nor of vocabulary weakness that mistakes *brake* for *break* and *effect* for *affect.* Nor even of stylistic devices, which must be handled with judgement.

Our problem here is the misspelling that betrays you twice over: you do not know how to spell the word correctly and have not troubled to find out. Too often, only the dictionary can give the answer. Rule books can't and even logic can't.

In the flush of writing the first draft you may not have wanted to reach for the dictionary to see what it decrees. With the Second Look, you do have time to check; after this stage, no excuse can purge the misspelling in your manuscript.

So own a good desk dictionary—and learn how to use it. This is not as absurdly obvious as it sounds. Too many use the dictionary only as a storehouse giving the meanings of words, with some synonyms thrown in for good measure. And even those who value it for its spellings often flip through it much too quickly. Take a half hour to familiarize yourself with its appendices, especially if it has one on orthography. Here, for example, you will learn not to fuss over *imbed* versus *embed*—they are equally correct. Even when the dictionary offers its "preferred" spelling quite firmly, remember common sense. It's a preference, not dogma. And who "prefers" it? And how many years ago did the dictionary note this preference? Times change—many good writers today prefer *instal* to *install, fulfil* to *fulfill.*

Self-editing—Your Guide

The self-editing pointers that follow are designed to help when you are taking the Second Look. For more about ambiguity, jargon, transitions, verbiage, etc., refer to the appropriate chapters elsewhere in this book.

1. Any misspellings? They are the most glaring fault. Spell a word the way you find it in a standard dictionary. That's the only license you need. If the word is not yet in the dictionary, choose the spelling favoured by somebody reputable in your field—or simply shy away from the word.

The rest is mainly a matter of being consistent (don't spell it foreign-style *metre* one time and American-style *meter* the next); and of being nonexperimental (prefer to be conspicuous by the brilliance of your ideas rather than by the avant-garde flashiness of your spelling).

2. Any boomerangs? Jove nodded, and Adam fell, and so do we all. After publication is too late—it's with the Second Look that you must catch face-reddening blunders. Blunders in spelling, yes, but there are various other embarrassments.

Remember that the written word has power to harm. You can sound derisive without meaning to: "He was the only geologist . . ." becomes insulting as "He was only a geologist . . ." "The glare of Florida sunshine" sounds like propaganda for California. An omitted word can be as injurious as an uttered one: The difference between "Smith stole Brown's patent" and "Brown claimed that Smith stole his patent" invites a libel suit.

Some mishaps are less dangerous but are embarrassing, like telling the reader to see an accompanying chart that is not there. Other mishaps, and this kind is an occupational hazard of the writer who writes a book on how to write, might contradict what the writer is preaching. For example, if I inveighed against "excess verbiage," I would be letting a cliché trap me into committing the sin of tautology. There the word *excess* is itself verbiage. To take liberties with another cliché, I would be blowing myself up with my own petard. "The junction of parallel lines leading to the vat" and "Where latitude is latitude and longitude is longitude, and never the twain shall meet" are examples of moments that writers would prefer to forget. They are the price paid for uncritically borrowing a stock expression or for playing carelessly with words.

Overhasty mathematics can be treacherous too: "They slashed their prices by some 300 per cent" cannot mean that; and "doubling the horsepower" does not add up to "200 per cent more horsepower."

3. Any factual unreliability? Accuracy is our business. In its simplest form it avoids calling a whale a fish and realizes that *engine* is often not synoymous with *motor*. It consults the dictionary, when in doubt, for the difference between *factor* and *feature*, *average* and *mean*. It pounces on possibly dubious borrowings from other jargon, changing the statistician's ". . . up 168 from 1959" to ". . . 168 more than in 1959." And, of course, remembering that spelling bloomers can occur in many ways, it checks to make sure the secretary has not innocently changed "humane being" to "human being."

4. Any two-faced words? Ambiguity not only violates clarity but often makes us ridiculous. Sometimes the real culprit here is jargon. For example, a secretary was teased so much when she answered the telephone with the words "Human Engineering Division" that she disregarded instructions and changed to a simple "Hello." Other times we don't keep related words near enough to each other: "Here are details of 7 vibration isolators using coil springs digested from an English technical paper."

The rest are simply words that face two ways: "Patient care in the hospital" (is *patient* adjective or noun?); "Russia's smallest satellite" (a country or a sputnik?).

Reading your paper aloud often makes such blunders loom large. It also helps when you write for oral delivery. "The building was razed" is satisfactory for the printed page. But if it's in a speech, most listeners would first think of "raised." Safety suggests changing to "The building was razed to the ground."

5. Proper punctuation? Like bad spelling, bad punctuation betrays haste and sloppiness. Look for the common trouble-makers. For example, remember the nuisance hyphen. We say "single ply" and "double ply" but the prefix demands "multi-ply" instead of "multiply."

The same need for common sense applies elsewhere. And

watch out for bad habits. In this book, the ellipsis marks (. . .) and italics are not brought in to make you gasp, but because they are needed. The first indicates omitted words; the second points to a word used as an exhibit. Otherwise, italicizing too many words would announce that the rest is negligible, just as too many exclamation points are noisily poor substitutes for finding the right word.

6. *Synonyms lacking?* It's monotonous to use the word *cancer* in every sentence. At the very least try such alternatives as *disease*. But that can be overdone too (see Chapter 7, page 110). Why not substitute something that adds to the meaning, like *malignant tumour*? That, in turn, opens the way to writing *the malignancy* and *the tumour*, depending on context. *Tumour* tells what it looks like; *malignancy* emphasizes its malevolence.

Remember, too, that synonyms offer a brisk way to translate jargon while adding information. No need to keep repeating "RP-1 and Lox." This can also be called *kerosene-oxygen mixture*, *missile propellant*, *explosive mixture*, *this powerful combination*, and so forth.

Similarly, when you refer to the author of *The Time Machine*, he need not always be H. G. Wells or just Wells. He can also be *this British writer*, *this pioneer in science fiction*.

7. *Sentences start badly?* Look hardest at the beginning of each sentence. Here is the dwelling of many frailties. The best example is the introductory phrase and, with it, the question: Comma or not?

a. The long phrase should have the comma. How long is *long*? When you are grateful for the pause. Example: "Despite the extreme care that was taken and the high cost of the experiment, they found that . . ."

b. Whether the opening phrase is long or short, it needs a comma if ambiguity or other awkwardness threatens. Each of these, though short, must have a comma: "After all, the time is not important . . ."; "When resins won't stick, check for impurities . . ."; "Before 1897, thermometers were hand-made . . ."; "Often, related fields become apparent in the search."

8. *Transitions in order?* Here, the Second Look focuses on the beginning of the sentence that opens a paragraph. It looks for reader aids such as "A good example is . . ." and "The answer came from a later set of tests."

Also look for the transition that fails because of ambiguity: "Should it, or any item from our catalogue, stimulate an idea, please let us know." The reader is braced for a question, but there is none; therefore recast: "This or some other item in our catalogue may stimulate an idea. If so, please let us know."

9. Antecedents out of order? For instance, whom do you mean by *it* and *they?* Look for this troublemaker at the beginning of a sentence. Example: "It eradicates the germs and stimulates the antibodies. They react to the vaccine quickly." (Who reacts? Who eradicates?)

Another form requires vigilance against danglers: "RCA has developed a new data recorder. Weighing only 37 pounds, the company reports that it may become standard equipment on all aircraft." (RCA is surely heavier than that.)

10. Any circumlocutions? Let's be frank. Did something *undergo burning?* Was it *subjected to conbustion?* Did it *exhibit flammability?* Or did it *burn?*

Remember you not only save space and add to clarity, but you also show better polish when you come right out and say what you mean—with active words instead of passive, concrete instead of abstract.

Let's be direct. Read the following and then ask yourself why it couldn't have started with "It is smaller . . .":

> For example, the encapsulation material is vacuum moulded into the stator wires. This provides better heat conduction from the wires so that for the same wattage and the same winding and bearing temperatures, the size can be smaller. With the smaller size the weight of the rotor is less, allowing a smaller diameter shaft. This allows a smaller bearing; the smaller bearing robs less of the magnetic iron from the stator so less iron is needed on the outside diameter. In other words, it is smaller. . . .

11. Words? Words? Number 1 in this check-list was bad spelling—the fault seen first. Last in the list are the heavier chores to be done when self-editing—chopping deadwood, ventilating the jargon, trimming the fat. These have been covered elsewhere. For a quick review, here are samples of what to pounce on:

a. Fatty phrases. "It was shown" is usually verbiage. But this can be turned into a useful transition this way, "It was also shown"; and, still better, "The investigation also showed."

b. Too many *whiches*. Example: "We object to statements which are made with a mental reservation." It should be *that*, not *which*, but why not just: ". . . statements made with a mental reservation"? Another example: "This is a vague statement which is not worthy of an expert in the formation of soil." Why not: ". . . statement unworthy of a soils expert"?

c. In general, hack at all sentences bowing under their own overweight. Keep a plentiful supply of full-stops handy. As you read your manuscript, insert one wherever you can sever an overlong sentence.

14

POPULARIZATION (AND HONESTY)

THE scientist who sits down with pen or typewriter is as eager for recognition as the advertising copy writer or magazine freelance writer. Each, for his own purpose—dollars, fame, advancement, self-fulfilment—wants to put down words that will benefit him. And each, despite any modesty, measures success by popularity—by how widely he is heard.

When we look closer and examine specific fields, the common denominator turns out to be some version of "What's the use of writing if you're not heard?" Here, for example, are five quite different situations that add up to much the same thing.

1. Suppose you want to report to the nation's farmers. This group is alert but doesn't pretend to know either the jargon or the so-called "scientific method" of biology, agronomy and such. Nor are farmers a homogeneous group. Cherry grower and Hereford rancher speak different lingos. So you are facing no easy task. The National Project in Agricultural Communications says:

> Write a technical report intended for this non-technical audience. Write the message as simply as you can. Dress it up as much as you dare. Interested non-technicians may look at it, but how many will read? How many will say, "It's too deep for me!"

2. Now hear medical researchers being spanked by The Federation of American Societies for Experimental Biology:

It has always been [our] policy to accept abstracts of all papers submitted, irrespective of their significance. In the past this has been a wide policy because it gave the researcher a chance to broadcast his knowledge. Unfortunately in recent years there has been a tendency to publish for the sake of publication. This applies to the whole field of medical science. Self-restraint by authors and a more critical evaluation by societies and editors will eventually be needed lest we get hopelessly lost in a wilderness of published research data which no machine can adequately record because it does not have the ability to discriminate or relate.

3. Wall Street, too, is aware of the need, and some financial people, of course, are eager to respond. Here is one of the resulting advertisements, by an agency that will tell you in which technological basket to lay your nest egg:

The semantics of science is frightening. . . . The investing public can't cope with a leaky tap. How can they understand the impact of technology on securities? Semiconductors, ultrasonics, thermoforming of plastics, microwave, the egghead triumphs. . . . It is impossible for the amateur to decipher the esoteric. . . . Our current letter reviews a number of enticing speculations.

4. Science staggers under about 25 billion words published each year, with the figure growing exponentially. To find what he needs in all this, the scientist hopes for translating and abstracting machines, but they can only make the jargon more cryptic. At an international conference in London, a delegate reported that out of 9,100 technical journals taken by the London Science Museum Library, 4,300 were not consulted at all in a given year. If the library's 87,000 readers expected to find nothing of interest in the 4,300, he suggested, "the sooner they cease publication the better." Another delegate blamed the high percentage of self-plagiarizing in the technical papers and wondered if the answer might not be to ration each research worker, allowing him to publish only one paper and one preliminary report per year.

5. American newspapermen widely agree that the ¦New York *Times* is the world's greatest newspaper, but that does not mean it is great every day in every way. Its more interesting mishaps with the written word are noted, as I've mentioned before, by T. M.

Bernstein, its assistant managing editor, in the "bulletin of second-guessing issued occasionally from the southeast corner of the News Room." He uses this bulletin to toss bouquets and brickbats among the reporters and editors. Among his pungent sermonettes is the one titled "Explain, Explain!":

> Whether your specialty is finance or fission, politics or paleontology, remember that the vast majority of your readers do not have specialized knowledge. Never take the attitude that "Hell, everybody knows what a velocity-modulated oscillator is."

These five examples speak of the need. And throughout this book we have seen that it can be met: with clearly thought-out sentences, precise words and less jargon—even when the reader is a fellow lodge member. Or, to answer one of the complaints above, discriminate and relate; boil it down and present it in palatable form.

NASTY WORD?

But isn't this popularization? And isn't popularization a nasty word? Among the pompous and stuffy, yes. It is understandable that the timorous scholar or inferior scientist will look suspiciously at the open-door policy—somebody coming through the door might ask a blunt question. But their defence mechanisms cannot halt a growing tide, the world's need to know.

Its need cannot be deflected by quibbling. For example, the *Nebraska State Medical Journal* complained against the "popularizing" writers of the "pornographic" press. It seems that these gentry, in no wise baulked by medical terms, had been drawing on medical research for articles dealing with "the area of the human body bounded above by the iliac crests and below by a line drawn through a point just below the great trochanters of the femurs."

What the "pornographic" press was guilty of was not popularizing but sensationalizing. One explains, the other brays. The principles of popularization are highly compatible with those of good writing; and also of democracy, which need not be defended here. Popularization makes the facts understandable to the many. Some technicians have learned how. Others have not. It is the latter, and also some downright rascals, who mourn that popularization degrades integrity or sneer that the writer with readers is a "hack." This is sour grapes—or rascality.

Even if this attitude is nothing more than secretive intellectualism, I need only point out that the improvement of communication has become one of the holier missions of today's science, that it now has the official sanction of the American Association for the Advancement of Science. In a report published in 1960, covering four years of study, this group pointed to the large number of scientific matters—new problems of medicine and war, to name a few—that have become public matters. It went on to urge its members and affiliates to become better informed themselves and to supply laymen with the quick, understandable, reliable facts needed for intelligent decisions.

This policy need run into no serious problems of communication. In moving back and forth between the fields of science and communication, I learned long ago to disbelieve two extremes of pedantry:

That to be accurate you have to be boring.
That to be informative you have to sacrifice the truth.

Those are false pennants flying in a sham battle. They are alibis that impeach the tedious writer, on the one hand, and the unprincipled writer, on the other. Either type stands in need of prayer—and lessons in better writing.

Why let yourself be forced to the extremes? The choice is not between vulgarizing and bowdlerizing. The answer is authentic popularization, which makes the facts understandable to the many.

Agreed that popularization can degenerate into lies, or nonsense, or unprofessional "hard sell." But the lay public, with its reputed penchant for playing sucker, is not the only victim of such aggression.

Science-minded people, too, are being pulled and tugged. Increasingly, in their professional reading, physicians and surgeons are served advertisements as absurdly graphic as any of the pill-pushing ones on television—nubile young ladies stretching with muscular discomfort, weird neurotics in need of "calmatives," camel drivers scratching themselves and exclaiming in Arabic (helpfully translated to English): "Is there nothing to relieve my itching?" The medicos are exhorted to try and to buy: "The Age of Anxiety is upon is"; "The first FULL-RANGE therapy for chronic gout and gouty arthritis"; "THIS is the tablet that gives higher peak antibiotic blood levels"; "What lurks beyond the broad spectrum?" And a tranquilizer advertisement in a medical journal boasts that its pill gives "Alert Tranquility" to the busy executive (shown at his desk—in a wooded glade).

BUT IS IT HONEST?

From "hard sell" it is not far to slanting the facts and adjusting the data. Again, why blame readability? The fault is not that of popularization but of a professional group that should police itself and its pharmaceutical purveyors better, to prevent liberty from sinking into license.

Furthermore, it is no professional secret that truth is also poisoned by not popularizing—by the mumbo-jumbo of the esoteric. Technology has for some time been wryly deriding itself with codifications of what it calls Finagle's Laws. A sample: "No matter what result is anticipated, there is always someone willing to fake it." These "laws" are made operative by the introduction of such constants as K_f, the "Finagle" factor; K_b, the "Fudge" factor; K_d, the "Diddle" factor. To Finagle's Laws has been added a "Short Course for Research Writers" in which "accidentally strained during mounting" replaces "dropped on the floor" and "handled with extreme care throughout the experiment" replaces "not dropped on the floor." All this, in the satiric opinion of one critic can be boiled down to: "Any self-respecting engineer can sum it up with two really basic Laws—(1) If you don't know what you are doing, do it neat; (2) If you can't do it at all, write a report."

Let's speak plainly. Scientists are not supermen. Long before popularization, science had its percentage of people who did not live up to the moral standards of a humanistic Einstein or a patient Darwin, ". . . . that Abraham of scientific men—a searcher as obedient to the command of truth as was the patriarch to the command of God."

In his *The Study of the History of Mathematics*, George Sarton,

Harvard's noted historian of science, gently related some of his troubles:

> The account of their discoveries given by mathematicians—as well as by other scientists—should never be accepted without control. . . . The discoverer may be unconsciously led to exaggerate the difficulties, to minimize his own hesitations; his remembrance of various circumstances may be strangely garbled, and his final story as untrue, yet as innocent, as that of any honest angler reporting his feats. . . . The long and short of it is that the historian must always stand on his guard. "Seeing is believing" will never do. Seeing is not enough.

In other words, if some professional popularizers serve pot-boiled tripe, the jargonist, too, can be incompetent or an outright quack. Nor is this weakness limited to what the USSR calls the degenerating democracies. Faking seems as universal as truth. Not only have Moscow newspapers assailed the boredom in Russia's science fiction and such prose as "Nazarov shuddered. His eyeslits narrowed, his pupils flashing like darting fangs." They have also published the angry denunciation by leading Soviet physicists of "unconvincing, unscientific, irresponsible boasting by some of our colleagues about doubtful scientific theories that are discrediting all Soviet science."

It is also significant that today's tempo is fast erasing the image of a Herr Doktor and replacing it with that of a brisker personality who may prefer fast motorboats to taking a walk with no other companion than his theorems, or who, at a wine breakfast, hatches a geophysical project to drill through the earth's crust, and calls it Mohole.

As with "pure" science, so with "applied" science. Formerly, the researcher and theorist held themselves higher than the engineer in the peck order of prestige and standards. Today, they and the engineer join in the R & D teams working for government, industry, and other sponsors demanding speedier technology. The principal difference seems to be that the engineers are sometimes franker. We find an engineering journal advising its readers that Darwin was a dope to have spent a dozen years checking his facts before publishing his theory of evolution—a fool because this delay was inviting somebody else to beat him to the announcement.

So we return to a scientific fact of life—that technicians do crave recognition. And it is not seemly for some of them, as part of their "ethics," to disdain popularization, to scorn the journalists —or pretend to. The fact is that when journalism might be too slow, scientists do not hesitate to scamper into print themselves. When Meitner and Frisch worked all night over the long-distance phone between Stockholm and Copenhagen, it was like a newspaper reporter and rewrite man composing a hot murder story. They wanted fast publication of their report in the British journal *Nature*. They couldn't claim they were first to split a uranium atom; they were racing to be first to confirm such fission.

All this proves nothing more sensational than that it is unscientific and unwise to equate all science with idealism, and that if grammar is needed for clear communication, so is honesty.

There is no need for me to "sell" the advantages of honesty. But here are some reminders. Neither science nor writing can thrive on facts that are suspect and theories that leak too much. And if outright dishonesty is bad, carelessness can be serious too. It means less chance that even your sincere effort will be convincing next time.

To the risk we can oppose a simple enough "law": Stick to the facts, and the truth will take care of itself.

IT CURES THE MEDICOS

The big requirement is to remove the obstacle that stuffiness erects against popularization. There can be two kinds of integrity, stuffy and otherwise. Why, then, cannot there be two kinds of popularization, capable and otherwise?

That speaking more openly need not be harmful can be seen by again taking medical science as an example. For a combination of reasons, it has been the least communicative, even most secretive, of the technical professions. It, and its journals, formerly shied away from the newspaper journalist because of his forthright way of getting to the guts of an abdominal matter. It was not many years ago when conversation between medical researcher and journalist was: "Who wrote those goddamn headlines anyway?" "Why do you think that everybody who works on a newspaper has to be a sonofabitch?"

The two professions now speak to each other more civilly. This change can be credited partly to missionary work by the National Association of Science Writers, partly to medicine's looking at itself more critically. As a result of freer communication, both the layman and doctor have benefited.

The professional writer who did an article called "Unnecessary Operations" for a popular magazine was bringing out what had remained buried in obscure research reports and connecting it with what doctors privately complained about but had themselves been reluctant—or unable—to write about.

Meanwhile, just as the layman has been unable to understand his doctor, the doctor has been bewitched and bewildered by the research professor. This, too, is changing. The increasing number of medical magazines has brought more competition for the reading time of the busy physician and surgeon. And this has focused attention on the need for improved writing. The result is a newcomer like *Medical World News*. To persuade the doctor to reach for it first, it carries articles with such titles as "Prostate Palpation Holds Hidden Danger," "Breakthrough in Cholesterol," "Two New Theories on Two Old Diseases." These promise facts lifted out of research and made to speak with interesting frankness.

The clear air of boldness does more than ventilate stuffiness. It also revives truth. It harks back to crusaders like Pasteur who called a germ a germ, and none of this nonsense that "Even water is a poison, you know, if you drink enough of it." And it reminds the profession of Alexander Woollcott's "I was preparing to be a hero . . . then I realized that the stand I had taken [against censorship] was nothing more than would have been made by any decent man with the courage of a diseased mouse."

One result is medical research reported in this refreshing fashion:

> . . . At about the same time another group of investigators published a paper which showed the results in coronary disease of the use of radioactive iodine—the "iodine cocktail." But what constitutes a cure from the point of view of this atomic cocktail group? Of the "cures" 47 per cent were dead before two years had elapsed. . . .

CALL IT QUALITY

The world of aches and pains offers the writer many readers. That of the intellect appeals to a smaller audience. But here, too, the better scholars try to gain maximum readership by getting down to earth. An erudite but readable paper by Princeton's Dr. S. Lefschetz begins:

> Since mathematics tends to infiltrate more and more into every science, it is a vast territory, and everyone may well ask for some guidance in the maze. The best that we can offer is a voyage of exploration to that distant planet, modern mathematics.
>
> Well, if it be a planet, its two polar caps are algebra and topology. . . .

A professional writer would want to unmix the metaphors, but the professor has done nobly. He has written to fellow scientists, without pomp or deadliness. He has learned the basic requirement: Attract the reader; don't repel him.

This simply confirms two time-tested beliefs: Honesty pays; quality pays. Though not synonymous, the two march closely together. Quality writing is clear writing that attracts the editor or reader. And it is trustworthy writing that will make him reach for you again.

Popularization becomes sinful only when it veers from either of those two pragmatic paths. For example, a magazine arranged for a series of articles by prestige authors, with the promise that their facts would not be mangled. But later a request came to one of the authors. He had referred to an equation by Descartes. Would he mind if the name was changed to Newton, a name known better to the public?

The fact that this can be matched by the research worker who beclouds the facts and conveniently omits unsatisfactory data doesn't exonerate the irresponsible popularizer. Both types of communicator should go to work as carnival barkers.

HOW TO BE RIDICULOUS

But let's be realistic. Honesty alone is not enough for quality writing. This is especially true when one popularizes science. Nowhere in writing is there more need for good judgement, because here, truly, the men are separated from the boys. Why this warning? Because it is dangerously easy to strain too hard. Let us glance at a few of the ways in which your effort to woo the reader can lead you into absurdities.

"Now hear this!" Sometimes the writer has the notion that the reader is stupid—so glinting little capsules of fact are thrown in to keep him awake and listening. At other times the writer finds himself with items left over that he doesn't want to waste. Either weakness results in *non sequiturs* and other misfits that leave the reader groggy. In the following passage from an article in the usually well-edited magazine *Fortune*, I italicize the bewildering superfluities:

> Then, in quick order, he synthesized cortisone, cholesterol, other steroids, strychnine, all biological molecules of large size and frightful complexity. *With a mind as cool and well-ordered as his pale-blue, grey, and white office with a single handsome Japanese print,* Woodward developed the theory of organic structure as it applied to synthesis *in a way that has made his laboratory a mecca for foreign students.*

Cross-gartered stockings. It is understandable that a fledgling writer will be drawn to the unconventional. This is not bad in itself if he has rich talent. If he hasn't, he is much safer playing safe. If he was a Johnnie who couldn't read, he probably can't write well either. So, unable to spell, he falls back on eccentric spellings; unable to punctuate, he patronizes the counters of the antigrammarians; lacking a vocabulary, he seizes on avant-gardisms. In short, he makes himself known by Malvolio's "trick of singularity"—by wearing cross-gartered yellow stockings. In aggravated form, this condition leads him to slip into his writing such shock-words as "snotnosed young engineer"; unable to write a competent title, he offers such dashing ones as "Nuts to You" and "It's Full of Hot Air." None of this, of course, is popularization. It's merely a juvenile form of writing delinquency.

In pictures too. If words lend themselves to tricks of singularity, illustrative material offers still more opportunity to run riot. A quick way to spot the difference between professional and amateur is to compare the pictorial portions of a magazine like

Life with those of the weaker industrial and technical journals. Too often, unable to get or to recognize suitable photographs, the amateur editor commissions hasty sketches of the "cute" type to lighten the atrocious prose. The result looks like an absurdly unfunny comic book. The offbeat intrusions are as anomalous as the seagulls and whales that young Whistler painted into the harbour charts he was preparing for the U.S. Coast and Geodetic Survey. He was dismissed—and this was good. The Survey got the workmanlike charts it needed; Whistler turned to his true bent.

Un-improvement. A simple definition of "hybrid corn" is" a cross of two or more inbred strains of corn." To the layman this is hardly an improvement over just "hybrid corn." But it is even less enlightening to attempt too much—to try covering the entire field of genetics in a couple of paragraphs bulging with "Let's consider four strains—A, B, C, D"—and then dragging in fertilization, pollination, chromosomes, dominance, segregation. To popularize without explaining is merely being garrulous. If space does not allow, it is better not to try.

Risks of translation. We all know the drawbacks of translating from a foreign language. An Arab newspaper headlines "U.S. Government Executes 90 Communist Employees." They had been fired—discharged. But that newspaper translated "to fire" as "to shoot."

Translation within our own language can be perilous too. It is a big sin to change the meaning of a specific technical word in an attempt to popularize, as did the writer who changed *fabricated* to *produced* in the sentence: "This polypropylene can be readily produced by injection moulding, in standard equipment, to yield parts that are tough and rigid." (Polypropylene is *fabricated*—made into parts—after being *produced* by an entirely different process.)

And it was useless for a press agent to change the technician's "hydrophobic silicones" to "water-hating silicones." The dictionary would have explained that *hydrophobic* means morbidly dreading water, not hating it. And even this would have been incorrect. These were simply water-repellent silicones.

Sensationalism. Analogy is a favourite device for scientific exposition. But it can be worked to death, especially when we brandish oh-my-god statistics. Measuring a millionth of an inch is not comparable to detecting one 25-cent piece in a stack of coins three times as high as the Empire State Building—and perhaps who cares? It was eye-opening to say that one H-bomb could release more energy than all bombs dropped in World War II, and go on to calculate that, in fact, it would top all explosions set off in all wars in history. But that stunt is now threadbare. So is much other quick-quiz data. We have lost our Adam-and-Eve innocence; we aren't startled any more to learn that the sun is 93 million miles away, and the 100 zeros in the ambitious word-coiner's *googol* no longer make us blink.

Too much breeze. For some reason, a large percentage of technicians think popularizing means "jazzing up" the material. The result is often absurd and usually noisy, as in "A new super shell has *slugged* its way into the family of Space Age metals." Or, from a college catalogue this description of a course on Popular Culture:

> The care and feeding of this sometimes diverting and always over-whelming creature, which spawns in vacuum tubes, lives on paper and casts its shadow on countless screens, is the subject of this course.

Sometimes the result is a rather pathetic resorting to clichés, such as calling every human ailment a "dread disease" or, after a thousand words of heavy jargon, inserting the thoroughly anomalous "As we embarked on the grail-like quest. . . ."

At other times the subject disappears in the dust of stampeding words:

> Such headings serve as road signs, forcing the writer to keep his paper sharply organized and not wander like a drunken driver through traffic-laden streets, coming up sharp at dead ends, crashing to complete stops against unforeseen obstacles.

WHO MAY POPULARIZE?

Everybody. Anybody who is willing to doff the magician's mask. Anybody who realizes that science is moving too fast to tarry with the muffled meaning of mumbo-jumbo.

Who will succeed best with popularization? The writer who can:

▶ Recognize the ridiculous in an announcement like this one:

> A marshmallow biscuit has been devised with a porous base, which enables interior and exterior pressures to equalize and so prevents chocolate fatigue on the outer skin.

Chocolate fatigue? Well, those biscuits were served to air passengers and made a mess—they exploded at altitudes above 5,000 feet.

▶ Practice self-restraint, avoiding such excesses as:

> It seems almost dead certain that research labs. of the Niagara Frontier now moving into the area will proliferate. To add icing to the cake, technical data has been . . .

Proliferate is strain enough without *almost dead certain*. And take off the icing.

▶ Shun the jargon of every creed, recognizing it to be the same time-wasting nonsense as it is in this parody:

> To put it simply, without this ectoplastic emolufication one will usually wind up with protonic amalgamation, which is generally considered to be detrimental.

▶ Shed the superiority complex that afflicts many technicians. Even so reputable a syndicate as Science Service (founded and controlled by the National Research Council, National Academy of Science, and the American Association for the Advancement of Science) has encountered such snobbishness. Complaints have come in: "Your news that appears in the newspapers is inexact and no good. Why don't you write it as it appears in the AAAS journal *Science?*" The fact is that the stories from Science Service were identical with those in *Science*, word for word.

▶ Learn how to write better. This need is described by a spokesman for Army publications in "Why Can't Dr. Johnson Write?":

> This is a worry to Dr. Johnson. Why, with his Ph.D. magna cum laude, cannot he report his findings so that his colleagues can follow his work? Why did Bill Adams quit his job when he found that monthly reports would be required? Why can't Col. Jones say

"Yes, you may buy a new microscope" in less than two pages, single-spaced?

This is why how-to-write articles are read so avidly in science and engineering journals. It is why so many specialized new writing courses are opening at the universities, why industry sends its technicians to writing seminars and also publishes its own quick manuals for guidance. It is why even government bureaus have begun to teach science writing—notable here is the Department of Agriculture, which has gone so far as to set up a graduate school that offers courses in writing and editing to the entire government.

HELP WANTED

The growing need for communication cannot wait for all scientists and engineers to learn how to write effectively. And there is an added problem: How much time can they spare for writing? One result is the "Help Wanted" advertisements you see in newspapers and magazines. A fast-growing new profession is moving in to fill the need. It is composed of middlemen who translate the dialects of the various sciences.

There is no single job classification for these people. They are technical writers, public-relations people, science editors. They are the full-time science writers whom the Council for the Advancement of Science Writing wants to see on every metropolitan daily—popularizers, not sensationalists.

Advertising, too, has seen the need and gone direct to the public and the buyer with messages, written in improved prose and even in free verse, about nuclear power plants and spaceships. Melvin Brorby, a spokesman for advertising, calls for "the humanizing of the scientists and the simonizing of the humanists. A new kind of communication-scientist must be developed, a new corps of interpreters must be trained."

Always there is an echoing of the same thought in different words: The need to know can be met only by popularizing. We once had such renowned lecturers as John Ruskin. In more modern times the *Saturday Evening Post* has published an "Adventures of the Mind" series in which science, philosophy and the arts gracefully take their places side by side.

And zoologist George S. Fichter demands in *The American Scientist* that the technician cooperate by giving information to the new interpreters:

> Research scientists seem, as it were, to hoard the results of their investigations. Their findings remain too long the exclusive property of academic circles. Their new knowledge is disseminated so slowly that it is often obsolete by the time it escapes the technical journals.

The world of books, too, needs and is attracting skilful writers on science. Some are giving us accurate but easier texts for schools and colleges. Many are neatly putting the planets, the atoms, the heroes of science into a growing variety of avowedly popularized books, for children, for adults curious about this new world.

And science fiction? Well, why not?

It is only partly true that this fiction "is a new and sinister folklore in which the latest facts from the Massachusetts Institute of Technology are superimposed on a human insight hardly more developed than that of bushmen." When science fiction deals with imaginary universes, it tends naturally to become a vehicle for social criticism and for construction of inspiring utopias and counter-utopias.

Moreover, some of this fiction is not only astounding but astonishingly well written. It has other credentials too. A Purdue survey showed that of the 18 leading science-fiction writers, eight had degrees in science or engineering (two had Ph.D.'s in chemistry); four were working in technical professions. One, of course, is the researcher and professor of biochemistry, the prolific writer Isaac Asimov. He has published fluent textbooks and *The Intelligent Man's Guide to Science* as well as his long string of science-fiction successes.

Asimov is one example of what is being called the generalist, the modern Renaissance man. Today's technology, despite specialization—perhaps to overcome the drawbacks of its parochialism—is finding an increasing volume of writing work for these people of several talents.

Their writing ability and all-round alertness can overcome any lack of technical specialization. And they are more likely to

conquer jargon than be its slave. Some do nicely without any
technical background at all. Listen to the success story of
advertising writer Howard G. Sawyer, in the magazine *Advertising
Agency*:

> Me, I'm so little engineering-minded, I couldn't sharpen a pencil.
> I have to have my secretary come in to operate my Venetian blinds.
> . . . A production man in a paper mill knows chemistry. But he may
> know nothing about electronics. I find out from the electronics
> man and tell it to the paper man. . . . So be sure the writers like
> me are as dumb as me—because the guy we're all trying to sell
> may be just as dumb as me. And if he isn't, no harm. Tell it to the
> Sawyers, the Einsteins will understand.

There are many such middlemen, some with technical background but many with little or none. They carry such titles as
technical-information specialist, literature scientist, presentation
editor, publication engineer, engineer-journalist. Some work in
public relations, preparing speeches and releases; some serve as
writers and editors with house organs; some help the technicians
of industry, government and university to turn research findings
into presentable reports and articles.

And then there is a new and special breed of engineering
writer who is being avidly sought by technology. This is the
so-called "technical writer," whose work is largely the important
modern-day chore of writing manuals, specifications and handbooks. A company that experimented by hiring five of them had
to employ 500 a few years later. There are several thousand in
the aviation industry alone.

Yet it is not clear just yet what a technical writer is, nor are all
of them paid as highly as would be indicated by advertisements
promising salaries that are "Crazy, Man, Crazy." Most valued in
this class is the person who can translate good science into good
writing. But the combination, technical knowledge and skilful
writing, is a superspeciality that specialized education is only
beginning to learn how to handle.

A few companies have insisted upon both credentials and
been willing to pay accordingly. Others do what they can with
on-the-job training and postgraduate schooling that teaches writing

to the technician and science to the English major. A surprisingly large number of technical writers have come in "through the back door"—with little or no science in their background—and have picked up enough jargon to get by. When their writing doesn't go beyond the repeating of jargon, the results are what might be expected. It is bad writing even for a heavily technical manual. And when the interpreter is assigned to write "in general terms for a wide audience," here is one result:

> Under control of a stored program, an appropriate stimulus generator is selected and adjusted. The stimulus, directed to the proper missile umbilical wire, elicits a response from the missile sub-system. This response returns to ACRE, where it is digitized and evaluated on the basis of stored test limits.

However, standards are being raised; and the Society of Technical Writers and Publishers has become keenly interested in the problem of qualifications. At first glance, the requirements would seem to rule out the ordinary good writer with only an B.A. degree. But the belief is growing that it may be easier to teach the language of science to a capable liberal-arts person than to teach a science major how to write well. And we see an increasing number of advertisements like these: "Journalism, English, or engineering degree necessary"; "If you possess a B.A. degree in English or journalism, or a B.Sc. degree in chemistry or engineering, we may have just the opportunities you are seeking."

Much of the debate therefore becomes meaningless. Whether the technical writer comes from the science or English corner of the campus matters less than his having a reasoning mind and ability to explain. Here, then, is a new speciality which isn't so highly specialized after all. It isn't so much being "strong in science and weak in English," or vice versa, as having what a good writer and a good scientist share—awareness of the reader and willingness to work for clarity. It is unfortunate for either scientist or writer to fall into error like this:

> The extract was injected into several mice, which died within two to six minutes. Given smaller doses, the mice recovered.

15

YOUR CHOICE OF STYLE

AN imaginative craftsman takes command of his words and writes, "Protoplasm is a handful of dust that God enchants."

Another person, an encyclopedia writer, marshals a calmer grouping of words and says it this way, "Protoplasm is the fundamental material of which all living things are composed."

Neither sentence is complicated; in fact, the two are quite similar architecturally from the opening subject to the closing phrase. Neither expresses an unwieldy thought; some might even claim that here are two versions of the same simple statement.

Yet it would be ridiculous to deny a difference, and a sharp one. The first definition soars. The second is down to earth.

Which is better prose? I can only say that both show nice workmanship. Beyond that, each writer to his own. Each is addressing a quite different audience, so his version is quite different. That is, each sentence has what we call a different style.

Is it the sentence, or the writer, who has the distinctive style? Could the same person who framed one of the definitions of protoplasm have written the other also? And just what is style anyway? Must the choice be between rhapsodist and realist? Or between æsthetic Henry Adams and hairy-chested Hemingway?

And is this an esoteric debate closed to "nonliterary" outsiders? Why can't we also judge a technical report, a project memorandum, a science article or a new-product announcement by its literary effectiveness?

Or is style something else? Is it the level of your writing skill—command of vocabulary, ability to phrase clearly as well as effectively? If so, can it be weighed and measured? For example, can you be judged by whether you shoot staccato sentences at the reader or make him stagger under a 100-word sentence beginning with "Because . . ."?

And what about stylistic devices? Isn't style also characterized, for instance, by whether you teeter on high heels with words like *fabulous* or stumble with atrocities like *amplitude-wise*? by whether your manuscript is fly-specked with asterisks that detour the reader to phalanxes of discouraging footnotes?

We now see why the word *style* is a nuisance and why, throughout this book, I have not allowed it to monopolize our attention. It's a word for which there is no settled definition, an all-things-to-all-men word that would be banned in a semanticist's utopia.

But we live in a real world, and discourses on style forever buzz in our ears. Why does one writer say, "It makes me happy," while another says, "I could claw myself for pleasure, like the Cook of Chaucer"? The difference seems mainly in the dramatic verb *claw*. But, again, is it also in the chromosomic make-up—the type of personality who reached for that verb?

What, then, about style, which is apparently several things? How much is it the you that can never change, how much the you that can learn? But first, is style worth fussing over?

That depends on who you are. At one extreme is the kind of professional who has found a groove and travels contentedly in it. He may be writing chemical abstracts, or churning out science fiction. No matter—the field suits him and his mode of writing satisfies him.

Midway is the meeting ground between two large self-improvement groups. From the laboratories come the ambitious technicians who have already done some writing but want to become more literate and more interesting. From communications come the writers and editors who find it practical to learn the language of science. Both groups are still plastic enough to change "style."

At the other extreme are those beginners—writers and technicians alike—who spend too little time on actual writing, too much on fretting about the hairdo: "Shall I change my style?" "Will I spoil my style?" They can hardly be blamed because when they consult teachers or read the professional critics they find that tastes differ, that much of the discussion is jargon.

Some scepticism is helpful here. True, like any other art, writing has its open warfare between conservatives and radicals, and its uneasy frontiers between workmanship and showmanship. These are serious differences. But writing also has its nonsense quarrels over "form," and therefore its multitudinous recipes for style; too many dictums that you can't join the singing club unless you're a nightingale, or, conversely, that you can't earn a living unless you push a barrow; too much mumbo-jumbo about this writer's being lucid while the other is pellucid; too many masters' theses written on Gertrude Stein's obscurantic "A rose is a rose is a rose..." or on Praetorius' noble "Lo, how a rose e'er blooming..." or on Shakespeare's impassioned "a rose by any other name..."; too much about masculine style, feminine style—and the ambiguous sex of the dadaists; too much of the "almost arrogant intellectualism, the preoccupation with criticism, with philology, and with symbolism" that Dr. Julius Stratton, president of Massachusetts Institute of Technology, blames for what he calls the growing sterility of America's science as well as its literature.

STYLE—YOUR STYLISMS

If style to you means mainly stylistic devices, and these mean the loud novelty-words and latest clichés, then the problem is simple. Common sense and good taste tell you to spurn them.

But if you want guidance to useful stylisms—abbreviations, methods of displaying words, etc.—the answers can be had. Aided by the dictionary if you are a writer, and a reliable style manual if you are an editor, you quickly learn whether it is good practice to abbreviate this or that word and whether or not to capitalize the first *r* in *roentgen ray*. If you write much for publication, you soon learn that such stylisms vary from one publisher to another. But this isn't serious. The editor handling your copy will make the necessary changes.

However, much depends on your knowledge of your own field, and you will find it helpful to keep reminders handy. The simplest way is to supplement an already existing list. For example, lists of compounded words are many. Choose one that roughly meets the hyphening problems of your field, then make changes or additions as circumstances require. Similarly, there are many lists of abbreviations. Start with one that includes the abbreviations of physics, if you are a physicist, or of biology, if you are a biologist. Then emend the list—make it your very own. Likewise, if you are in chemistry or some other materials field, work up a handy list of trade names and those that have become generic, so that you will remember to capitalize *Teflon* but not *nylon*.

Consistency here is a virtue—and proofreaders will bless you for it. The man who always signs himself "X" is illiterate but helpful. On the other hand, General Electric has been unable to make up its mind whether to abbreviate itself to G-E, G.E. or GE.

In a sense the symbols and mannerisms of specialized writing are stylisms too. For example, technical writers now have a wide choice of specialized textbooks. In them you learn how to assemble handbooks and manuals, how to arrange tabular material, how to compose a list of specifications.

Whatever the type of stylism, it is only a single, narrow aspect of writing, and a collection of stylisms is but a small third of what we usually mean by style. The need for ordinary, capable writing is what faces most technicians. It is not from a hunger for stylisms that the readers of one engineering magazine sent in 20,000 requests for reprints of hasty one-page lessons on how to write.

STYLE—YOUR CRAFTSMANSHIP

Dig into the problem deeper; equate style with the over-all mechanics of writing, as teachers commonly do, and we are much nearer the definition. Like stylisms, this element, too, can be taught and learned. Of course, the definition is still rather elusive. A dedicated scholar calls it "the application of rhetorical principles." And usually sharp-tongued Dean Swift couldn't do better than the often-quoted "proper words in proper places" (but who is to decree what's proper?).

Both definitions equate style with grammar; neither indicates that styles may differ. For example, some good writers use "open" punctuation—only the marks absolutely necessary for understanding; others favour the more meticulous "close" punctuation. Which is better? Whichever you handle best. Handled illiterately, both produce illiterate writing.

Each extract below is from a different corporation's annual report. Note the usage of hyphens—one way to judge tightness of punctuation:

> The division also announced a line of batteries specially designed for use in transistorized portable radios and cordless home radio sets. Another addition to our battery family is a group of rechargeable batteries with hermetically sealed nickel-cadmium cells.

> Stereophonic sound—the full dimensional reproduction of high-fidelity music—reflects a steady rise of popular interest in quality music listening. Its impetus is expected to boost the all-important recorded music industry's business well over the billion-dollar mark.

The first example suavely gets by with only the one, needed hyphen. The second stumbles; it is a careless blend of "close" and "open" punctuation. Inasmuch as it used the three hyphens, why didn't it, with equal punctiliousness, also write *full-dimensional*, *quality-music listening*, *recorded-music industry's*?

A practical approach is to lay aside the word *style* and substitute *good writing*, as I have done often in this book. Nor am I alone. When Cornell's William Strunk years ago wrote his admirable *The Elements of Style*, he apparently chose the title for convenience. His main purpose was to teach his "18 rules of accurate, forthright English," which began with the workmanlike "Form the possessive singular of nouns by adding '*s*." Or listen to Quiller-Couch. When he tried to define style, he could only say that it "resembles good manners"; he then quickly got down to the business of slashing at "circumlocution rather than short straight speech . . . choosing vague woolly abstract nouns rather than concrete ones." And when I glance through the textbook from which I learned advanced rhetoric, I find that its index does not even mention style.

Let us agree that style, in the present context, refers to craftsmanship—wherever you find it. Good style cannot be subdivided into good writing for electronics, for biology, or for belles-lettres any more than we can safely equate good writing only with blind obedience to the dictates of pedantry. For, as Robert Burger of Dartmouth reminds us, writing that is impeccably grammatical can also be "unbearably dull, extravagantly inefficient, outrageously—and quite unnecessarily—difficult."

Consequently, science writing—though it requires us to handle a special vocabulary, though it forces us to emphasize clarity and accuracy—need not condemn us to deadliness. With respect for the right word, with workmanlike leads, with suave transitions, we can also be effective—we can persuade the reader to join us and stay.

For example, this opening sentence from a textbook, on technical writing, is hardly encouraging to the reader:

> The principles of rhetoric are generalizations based on the broadest observations of the human mind working systematically.

Contrast it with the opening sentence from another textbook, this one for advanced writing students, and see how much more incisively the author makes his point:

> The one fundamental obligation of every writer is to be clear; it is to his advantage to be also interesting and effective.

Style in this sense quickly loses any connotation of being only for a chosen, specialized few. The writing can be quite "popular." In his *The Phenomenon of Man*, Pierre Teilhard de Chardin tells us:

> Man came silently into the world. As a matter of fact he trod so softly that, when we first catch sight of him as revealed by those

indestructible stone instruments, we find him sprawling all over the old world from the Cape of Good Hope to Peking. Without doubt he already speaks and lives in groups, he already makes fire. . . . Thus in the eyes of science, which at long range only sees things in bulk, the "first man" is, and can only be, a crowd, and his infancy is made up of thousands and thousands of years.

Or it can be the meat-and-potatoes type of exposition in a service magazine for engineers. Here, after the workmanlike title, "Watch Out for Compression Loads," comes a capable lead:

An erroneous belief in design is that metals are always as strong in compression as in tension. This can lead to trouble, particularly where buckling loads occur. The fact is, tension and compression properties cannot be used interchangeably. The differences are important; they are characteristic of most metals in the worked condition, they appear in both sheet and bar material. . . .

Remember, too, that craftsmanship requires more than suitable phraseology. It must also "betray" that the writer has dug deeply enough for facts and therefore knows whereof he speaks. This is applicable to any expositional writing, and in any era. Listen to thunder rolling through the opening of Tacitus' *Histories*:

I am entering on a work rich in disasters, savage wars, civil strife; even its peace was cruel. Four emperors perished by the sword. There were three civil wars; more wars abroad, often both at once. . . . The seas were crowded with exiles; and rocky islets stained with murder. Rome itself saw cruelties yet more savage. . . . Such was the state of the Empire when Servius Galba assumed his 2nd consulship, with Titus Vinius for colleague, in the year that was to be their last, and came near being the last for Rome.

STYLE—YOUR PERSONALITY

The stylisms and disciplines of good writing can be learned. But there remains a third ingredient of style, and therefore a third ingredient of success. This is the element usually overlooked by rule makers. It is Style with the capital S—for example, the tendency to write staccato if you're a jitterbug at heart, to write sweepingly if you have a taste for mouthing rich words. It's an expression of what we call personality and cannot be changed any more easily than the surgeon can give you a new face. Even then the change is superficial because Style is largely the unchangeable, chromosomic you.

Admittedly, Style is also influenced by environment and the times. Where writers once were forced to be coy and say merely that a character uttered "a crimson streak of profanity," the cuss words and four-letter words today are so common that they are criticized less for their luridness than for their banality. But, in Chapter 1, page 13, note that the difference between Faraday's classic phrasing and the vigorous sentences by a present-day engineer is not so much a hundred years or the contrast between an Englishman and American as it is the difference between the optimism of one individual and the impetuous protest of another.

Or compare this Japanese poem:

My barn is burnt down—
Nothing hides the moon.

with Hemingway's "medical writing" in *Green Hills of Africa*:

"Bugs," I said to M'Cola in Swahili, speaking with strong disapproval.
"No," he said, dismissing the idea. "No bugs."
"Bad bugs. Many bugs. Sickness."
"No bugs," he said firmly.
The no-bugs had it. . . .

Neither passage wastes words. But the first is the delicate imagery of a hokku, the second is laconic prose.

And note that when Mark Twain discusses writing, it's the characteristic imp in him that fires an arrow into pomposity:

I like the exact word, and clarity of statement [now comes the twang of Twain's bow] and here and there a touch of good grammar for picturesqueness.

This third element of style—personality—does more than influence the tone of your sentences. It provides the framework upon which the other two elements are superposed. Even though you may be versatile, it governs your special suitability for a particular kind of writing. It helps decide whether you will be happier writing reports of your scientific research or journalistically reporting the work done by others; whether you will be more successful writing careful technical manuals or imaginative advertising; whether you might even be better off writing fiction. This is the first step—recognizing your bent. After this comes the self-improvement phase—learning tricks of the trade.

In any branch of writing, Style concerns the difference, often elusive, that challenges literary critics to bring out their best adjectives. Or, when a craftsman like James Thurber tries to describe the Style of another skilled workman, E. B. White, he finds that neither definitions nor adjectives will do, and lapses into his own good writing:

> Many of the things he writes seem to me as lovely as a tree—say a maple after the first frost, or the cherry hung with snow.

In any type of writing, too, because Style dwells so deep in personality, it also influences the writer's choice of topic, and his treatment of that topic. It therefore serves as a useful measure for comparing different writers working in the same vineyard.

For example, take two nonfiction classics: Edward Gibbon's *Decline and Fall of the Roman Empire* and Gustavus Myers' *History of the Great American Fortunes*. Each is the product of monumental research, each is derisive. Yet the two Styles do differ. Gibbon could afford to be urbane because he had retreated to ancient times. Myers chose to expose the ills of modern times and he gave them a rougher tongue-lashing.

Or, closer to our field, take fiction that deals with science. In his novel *Arrowsmith*, the nervous energy of Sinclair Lewis led him to rip aside camouflage and hypocrisy in medical research. Compare this with the analysis of scientific chicanery by England's physicist-novelist C. P. Snow—a calmer writer with compassion for those torn between conscience and egoism.

We find such variation, too, in the nonfiction of science. Einstein, writing about the universe, and Hans Zinsser, a noted medical researcher, writing about his own life, both revealed an inner serenity. Now contrast them with a pair of more critical authors, who are examining the concept of scientific method. The first extract is from Max Otto's *Science and the Good Life*; the second, from Anthony Standen's more tart *Science Is a Sacred Cow.*

> It would help us all to clarify our conception of science by doing away with a number of vital errors. One of these is a confusion between science as it actually is, and the aura of myth and legend which envelops it.

> Thus the world is divided into Scientists, who practice the art of infallibility, and non-scientists, sometimes contemptuously called "laymen," who are taken in by it.

There is, of course, a lurking danger in Style. An experienced writer can control this self-expressiveness with the disciplines of good writing. The beginner, however, may see here a license to exaggerate his own importance. For example, it is quite human to have a repressed desire to write editorials—and for beginners to succumb to the temptation to editorialize. But even an out-and-out editorial must not be an egoistic picnic. Nor can it be a labour-saver that lets you just run on and on, with words substituting for facts.

Other traps await the beginner. He may feel that Style frees him from the standards of good taste, or from the need to translate jargon. And, of course, it's easy to overdo the advice "Just write the way you talk," which can be a shortcut to acquiring the reputation of being a barbarian. Deadliness, no. But there's no hurt if a bit of education breaks through occasionally.

READING HELPS

The best way to improve over-all writing style is by writing. But as in any art, you need aids. One of the most important of these is reading.

Not just textbooks on writing—they can only be a guide and reference; not just books in your own technical field—these you read principally for their factual content; not just reading to speed your reading so that you can keep up with the facts you need; not just reading to stretch your mind, or your vocabulary.

I am speaking simply of exposure to good writing, the good writing by others. This is the learning method that is sometimes and erroneously called osmosis. It is more technically correct to call it a soaking-in process.

It develops your "writer's ear." When you "hear" the word *implicit* in correct context often enough, you will not confuse it with *explicit*. When you see how safely *partly* can substitute for *partially*, you will dare adopt *partly* too. When you read a capable writer you will find him saying "I will try to make it work" instead of "I will try and make it work"; "depends on" instead of "is dependent on." Expose yourself to enough of such writing and it will influence your own.

Certainly this is an effective way to nail down grammar. For example, I know no better way to absorb the logic of verb tense. And the cure for the common trouble-makers, such as bewilderment over whether to write *is* or *are*, becomes something imbedded in you. Or, rather, it becomes something on the tip of your tongue. It becomes habit, idiom, instead of a rule that you may have trouble defending.

If logic and rules cannot always handle dilemmas growing out of tense and number, your predicament becomes worse when punctuation problems arise. We know, for example, that a certain pause calls for a comma. But how long, how "loud" a pause? The rules also prescribe the comma as a clarifier. But it is you who must recognize ambiguity and then decide where such a comma will do most good.

While it is improving your writing, reading is also improving your reading. This is not as complex as it sounds. There are two ways to read.

One is the method of the "slow reader"—studying, tasting each word. This is the result of a word-by-word method of teaching youngsters how to read. For the adult it has its usefulness when words are very technical. It is also the method, of course, by which editors do the painstaking part of their work on manuscripts and proof.

But good editors, like all good readers, have a second method. This is the scan technique, reading by expressive phrases rather than word by word. It is much faster, of course. Its other value is that it allows your "inner ear" to listen in terms of context. When you read by blocks of words you automatically supply a comma after "anticipated" in "No matter what result is anticipated there is always someone willing to fake it." And a comma automatically inserts itself after "popularization" in "Even with the trend toward popularization science remains a mystery to many laymen."

The more you read good writing, then, the more practice you get in such scanning and the sooner your own writing shows better phrasing.

Furthermore, reading develops the writer's eye as well as his ear. It is the best way to become a capable speller without torturing oneself with rules. When you see *believe* and *receive* often enough, you need not fumble for the "*i* before *e* except after *c* rule." If you are exposed often enough to competent hyphenation you will acquire good taste in such things—you will not blindly follow a rule and write the grammatically acceptable but forbidding *deaeration*; you will also know that *microorganism* is quite legitimate.

In other words, your own writing style will become based on a stock of precedents and analogies, and this will help make you a master of the rules which, we know, are nothing more than a writing down of what is good usage.

With all this, you can absorb something even harder to teach than rules of grammar, and harder to learn—a familiarity with nuances of meaning. For example, there is a subtle difference when "I cannot see" is changed to "I fail to see." Or consider the phraseology of consent which is so important when you write a letter or memorandum. Each of the following says the same thing, but with an important difference.

We will be willing to . . . (a reluctant concession)
We would like to . . . (if you approve)
We will be happy to . . . (beaming with cooperation)

It matters little what you read, if it is good writing. It is not difficult to find good writing—one of the characteristics of quality is that it usually speaks for itself. All fields have their better grade of writing, and advertising is no exception. Believe or disbelieve the claims, as you wish, but concede that here is a form of communication which can be both clear and persuasive. It led poet

Robert Frost to exclaim, "I'd rather read the advertisements in *Scientific American* than most literature written elsewhere." Or listen to Aldous Huxley, another craftsman in his own right. Back in the 1920s he announced that he had

> . . . discovered the most exciting, the most arduous literary form of all, the most difficult to master, the most pregnant in curious possibilities. I mean the advertisement. No one should be allowed to talk about the *mot juste* or the polishing of style who has not tried his hand at writing an advertisement of something which the public does not want, but which it must be persuaded into buying. Your *boniment* must not exceed a poor 100 or 150 words. With what care you must weigh every syllable! What infinite pains must be taken to fashion every phrase into a barbed hook that shall stick in the reader's mind. . . .

And, of course, there are the good and "great" writers. Go back to the sonorous sentences of Francis Bacon and the other classicists. Or read the moderns. Any kind of good literature, sober or refulgent, will serve. If you prefer to stick closer to our field, there are not only the new books on science but an increasing number of armchair anthologies that include both scientists and professional popularizers.

Your reading will be the more helpful if you do it with the attitude of one writer appraising another, remembering that the other had his troubles too, that even the Stylist often has to struggle with the raw materials. For example, the original manuscript of Walt Whitman's *Leaves of Grass* shows that his beginning went through a tortured evolution of a dozen stages—substitutions of words, crossing-out of entire lines—before "Go, said his soul to a poet/ Go, write me such songs . . ." became "Come, said my soul/ Such verses for my body let us write."

Nor need the reading be merely a soaking-in process. Note how one writer solves a transition, how another evades an ambiguity or devises a happy phrasing. When you see a neatly effective lead, tear it apart and see what makes it tick.

Then you can go even farther—and actually benefit from bad writing. When you see the dismal phrase "crack proneness," mentally change it to "proneness to cracking." When you see "A fuel cell is used to generate the electricity instead of a heat engine," jot down ways to eliminate that ambiguity.

Eventually you become somewhat of a literary critic. And you now realize that good style has become a synonym for quality, which is also hard to define but does have noticeable characteristics. Bad style—awkwardness, illiteracy and the rest—calls attention to itself. By contrast, quality is a lack of irritation. Unlike "flux-residue removal" it goes down smoothly, like ice cream down your throat. It's the careful tailoring one takes for granted in a fine garment; it's the motor you don't hear in a Rolls-Royce; it's Hamlet's advice: "Nor do not saw the air too much with your hand, thus, but use all gently . . . and beget a temperance that may give it smoothness." Even teen-agers respect it: "Cool, man, cool!"

For the science writer's danger always is an attempt to jump from the extreme of deadliness to the extreme of sensationalism. Science insists upon certain requirements—among them, an absence of error and an abhorrence of the obscure. For us, good style definitely cannot be the avant-garde writing of an abstractionist painter:

> As I'm walking down 14th Street with my Botticelli woman, her feet never touch the pavement. As I'm walking down the street babbling to myself there is always the danger of making sense, and when that occurs I have lost my dream.

Nor can today's science writer afford to fall into the pattern of the Sunday supplement writers of yesteryear. For example, the worthwhile research done on sharks sounds ridiculous when a release describes it in this manner:

> The recently popular skin-divers' pastime of "riding" sharks, or hanging on to their tails, is dangerous and foolhardy, the Shark Research Panel of the American Institute of Biological Sciences said today.

The science writer needn't strain that badly to be somebody else. If his prose sings ecstatically like the European nightingale, fine. If it sings like one of the more restrained thrushes, that can be exceedingly pleasant too.

But mainly, good style, like quality, is a lack of what bothers the reader. The craftsman in our field will be happy to be commended for his manner of writing but he can be quite content, too, if the reader stays with him to the last word. That means the writing is pleasantly palatable. It offers something worthwhile and does it clearly.

Bibliography

Baron, K. D., *Teach Yourself Spelling*, 1939, E.U.P.

Bartless, J., *Familiar Quotations*, 13th Rev. edn. 1956, Macmillan.

Betterton, K., *Teach Yourself To Write*, 1942, E.U.P.

Carey, G. V., *Mind The Stop*, 2nd edn. 1958, C.U.P.

Collins, F. H., *Authors' & Printers' Dictionary*, 10th edn. 1956, O.U.P.

Collins, V. H., *The Choice of Words*, (A Book of Synonyms) 1952, Longmans.

Chamber's Twentieth Century Dictionary, rev. edn. 1959, Chambers.

Fowler, H. W., *Modern English Usage*, 1926, O.U.P.

Fowler & Fowler, *The Concise Oxford Dictionary*, 4th edn. 1951, O.U.P.

Fowler & Fowler, *The King's English*, 3rd edn. 1930, O.U.P.

Freeman, W., *A Concise Dictionary of English Idioms*, 2nd edn. 1952, E.U.P.

Gloag, J., *How to write Technical Books*, 1951, Allen & Unwin.

Gowers, Sir E., *The Complete Plain Words*, 5th rev. imp. 1958, H.M.S.O.

Horwill, H. W., *A Dictionary of Modern American Usage*, 2nd edn. 1944, O.U.P.

Jepson, R. W., *Teach Yourself To Express Yourself*, 1944, E.U.P.

Middleton Murray, J., *The Problem of Style*, 1960, O.U.P.

Nicholson, M., *A Dictionary of American-English Usage*, 1957, O.U.P.

Ogden, C. K., (Ed.) *The General Basic English Dictionary*, 1940, Evans.

Partridge, E., *A Dictionary of Clichés*, 4th edn. 1949, Routledge.
    Usage and Abusage, 5th rev. edn. 1957, Hamish Hamilton.
    You Have a Point There, 1953, Hamish Hamilton.

Roget & Roget. *Roget's Thesaurus*, 1852, rev. paperback edn. 1953, Penguin.

Treble & Vallins, *The A.B.C. of English Usage*, 1936, O.U.P.

Index

243